WILDLIFE
OF THE WORLD

WILDLIFE
OF THE WORLD

TED SMART

This edition produced by Ted Smart
for The Book People Ltd
Guardian House,
Godalming,
Surrey, GU7 2AE

ISBN 1-85613-009-6

Manufactured in Spain

Producer : Ted Smart
Author : Rupert O. Matthews
Designer : Sara Cooper
Photo Researcher : Annie Price
Production Assistant : Seni Glaister

**The publishers wish to thank
Bernard Thornton Artists Ltd
for all the hard work and co-operation
that made this book possible.**

All photographs in this book
appear courtesy of the
Survival Anglia Photo Library

with the exception of the photographs on
pp 132, 154 and 156
which appear courtesy of NHPA

There is a truly astounding variety of wildlife in the world today. The result of millions of years of evolution, the thousands of species of mammals, birds, reptiles and amphibians which share our planet fill every conceivable niche in the natural scheme, and not a few that it would be difficult to imagine. There are great, lumbering beasts so huge as to make the ground shudder with their footsteps and others so light that they can scale a stem of grass without causing it to bend.

The endless procession of different types is amazing, all the more so when it is realised that all these creatures evolved from a basic stock hundreds of millions of years ago and that they have all evolved to live on the same planet. Nobody is entirely certain how many species there are alive today. This is partly because there are still unexplored wilderness areas where creatures unknown to science may live and partly because it is sometimes difficult to delineate where one species ends and the next begins.

This vast and wonderful array of life presents a magnificent spectacle, yet it is a frighteningly fragile edifice. The destruction being wrought on the rainforests, with large areas cleared each day, is well known but the effect on the wildlife is not always realised. As the forest vanishes the food and home of many creatures goes with it. Animals once common are now becoming rare, not because of hunting or trapping but simply because they have nowhere to live. It is not only the well-publicised rain forest where habitat destruction is taking place. Less exotic locations, such as European meadows or hedgerows are also being changed by the hand of man, and with their passing taking with them valuable habitats for familiar creatures.

Yet it is not a completely gloomy picture. In many areas natural areas have been set aside for wildlife and natural habitats are being preserved. Some animals, such as the tiger and panda, are the subjects of active preservation campaigns. There is hope yet that the wonderful display of wildlife available to us will still be there for future generations to enjoy.

The study of wildlife may be thought of as two interdependent disciplines. There is the study of animals in the field, where behavioural traits are noted and defined, and the more academic field of nomenclature in which the relationships between various species is considered. In this book both have been included in order to give as complete a view as possible of the wildlife of the world. The bewildering array of creatures is presented in scientific order, divided into groups and arranged according to the relationship which exist between them. Within this framework, the text concentrates on the lives of the creatures, their life cycles, appearance, capabilities and behaviour.

The pictures which accompany the text have been produced by a team of wildlife artists who have tried to portray the true beauty and individual interest of each group of creatures, and who have succeeded in their aim. This book is a catalogue, in words and pictures, of the truly magnificent wildlife of our wonderful world.

MARSUPIALS
The Pouched Animals

The curious and appealing monotremes or egg-laying mammals are often considered to be the most primitive of the living mammals because of the many differences between themselves and other mammals. However, it is more likely that the monotremes are an isolated side branch of mammalian evolution rather than the sole survivors of early ancestors. Monotremes are distinguished from other mammals by the fact that they lay eggs and lack distinct nipples. The mother's milk simply seeps through pores in the abdominal skin.

Whatever their evolutionary origins, the monotremes are found only in Australasia, where they are safe from competition from the more advanced placental mammals. The platypus is relatively common around streams and rivers in Tasmania and the lusher areas of eastern Australia. It is active at night, feeling its way through the mud of the river bed with its bill in search of invertebrates. The Platypus also has a liking for fish eggs, a trait which has brought it into conflict with salmon-farmers.

The curious appearance of the platypus, with a soft leathery bill, webbed feet and long body is today well known. But when it was first discovered and skins sent back to Europe, the scientists refused to believe that such a creature could exist. They thought that it was a fake stitched together by some Australian prankster.

The other common monotreme is the spiny anteater or Echidna, found through much of Australia and in parts of New Guinea. As its name suggests this 15 inch (38 cm) long creature bears spines and eats ants. The spines are defensive for when disturbed the creature rolls up to present a sharp hedge to enemies. When on soft ground the spiny anteater may dig itself into the ground to escape predators. It also uses its tough digging claws to rip open ants' nests. The anteater then flicks out its long sticky tongue to capture its prey. Some observers have seen the creature ignore the adult ants and to dig through to the nursery chambers where the soft-bodied larvae are found.

Marsupials, like monotremes, make up a distinctive order of mammals. In this case the distinguishing feature is that the females have pouches in which they carry their young. The young are born at a very early stage of development when they lack fur, are blind and often have only one pair of limbs. These near helpless infants crawl through their mother's fur to the pouch. Here they attach themselves to a nipple where they remain for some weeks. Only when fully developed do the young venture outside the pouch. Even then they continue to suckle and will dive back into the pouch at the slightest sign of danger.

Marsupials first evolved some 90 million years ago during the time of the dinosaurs. They were originally widely distributed throughout the southern continents while the more advanced placental mammals inhabited the northern lands. Though some small marsupials survive in South America, a full marsupial fauna is today to be found only in Australia. This great island continent has not been joined to other lands during mammalian times so the marsupials have been able to evolve free from competition with other creatures.

Perhaps the most familiar, certainly the most attractive, marsupial is the koala. With its furry ears and winning, wide-eyed face the koala has become a firm favourite with advertisers and toy manufacturers. It is totally adapted to life in trees, only coming to the ground to move on to a new tree. The strong grasping claws of the koala grip branches so tightly that it is almost impossible to remove a determined koala from its perch. The leaves of a few species of eucalyptus gum trees form the exclusive diet of the wild koala, though captive creatures eat a wider variety of foods.

The closely related spotted cuscus lives in New Guinea and is the most elaborately marked marsupial. Its patterned coat appears to be a camouflage, useful in the dappled light conditions of the forest. The much smaller Pygmy Possum also inhabits the New Guinea forests.

The marsupial which shows the most complete adaptation to an arboreal lifestyle is the great glider which inhabits the dense forests of eastern Australia. Living high in the trees, this creature feeds on the leaves and fruits of the forest, scampering through the trees with the

1: *Greater Glider.*
2: *Koala (2).*
3: *Spotted Cuscus.*
4: *Bush-tailed Possum.*
5: *Platypus.*
6: *Pygmy Possum.*
7: *Spiny Anteater.*

Left: A female koala with her young clasped to her chest. When too large to live in the pouch young koalas cling to their mother's fur until they are old enough to fend for themselves. Below: A brush-tailed possum from Queensland, Australia.

aid of its clawed feet and prehensile tail. When facing danger, the greater glider lives up to its name by flinging itself into thin air and gliding to a nearby tree or the ground. When gliding it stretches out its four limbs, pulling taut a flap of skin between its fore and hind legs which acts as a parachute.

Most marsupials have suffered from the spread of civilisation through Australasia during the 19th and 20th centuries. Only the brushtailed possum has increased in numbers. In its native state the brushtailed possum was an opportunistic feeder taking any plant or animal food it could find. It has recently moved into towns, adapting to feeding on refuse and food scraps left by humans.

Perhaps the most outlandish marsupials are the kangaroos. These amazing creatures stand on two legs and move by great bounding leaps which can power them at amazing speeds. At full stretch the larger species can cover 35 feet (11 metres) in a single bound. Early settlers hunted kangaroos on horseback with the aid of dogs for sport. One famous run covered 18 miles of chase, a swim across a sea strait to an offshore island and further pursuit. When cornered, the kangaroo managed to kill one of the pack before it was shot.

Kangaroos are well adapted to their life on the arid plains. They need to cover large distances quickly and easily in search of food and water. The bounding gait is the most economical for high speed in terms of energy consumed. Most kangaroos are grazers, feeding on the grasses of the arid plains, though several species are browsers. The long, thick tail is useful as a 'third leg' when the creature is resting and serves to balance the body when the kangaroo moves at speed.

The largest kangaroo of all is the red kangaroo which can be over 5 feet (1.7 metres) in length and weigh over 200 pounds (90 kg). It is to be found across much of central Australia, inhabiting even the most arid areas. In some districts they are so numerous that they are considered a pest by sheep farmers who see their pasture

being consumed by the kangaroos.

There are nearly 60 species of kangaroo, but only a minority of them are referred to as such. The smaller species are referred to as wallabies. The yellow-footed rock wallaby lives in the more inhospitable regions of central Australia. It hops around rocky hills and craggy outcrops, finding safety in the broken country. It feeds on any grasses and bushes which find a roothold in the harsh environment.

In common with other species, the yellow-footed rock wallaby is susceptible to the periodic droughts which affect the area. When water and food become scarce the females reject suckling young to conserve their energy. If the drought persists adults begin to die, but there are usually enough left to recoup losses when the rains return. Most females carry a fertilised but dormant embryo in their bodies so that a new young can be born as soon as possible after fresh food appears.

The few species of kangaroo which inhabit forests are very different from their lithe, agile plains relatives. The red-legged pademelon lives in the damp forests of coastal Queensland and is a squat creature which moves slowly through the forest night in search of fruits and shoots. Even more squat is the quokka of Western Australia. It lives in dense undergrowth but has been known to move into human settlements in search of food scraps.

The hairy nosed wombat is both the largest and most numerous of the three species of wombat, or native badger, found in Australia. It measures over 4 feet (1.2 metres) in length and is common in the eastern forests where it browses on vegetation and fruits. Modern wombats are great burrowers, retreating to extensive tunnels during daylight hours. About 100,000 years ago the wombats included a much more impressive beast known as *Diprotodon* which was about the size of an ox. Indeed, many groups of marsupials produced giant species at this time. The fact that Australia was enjoying a cooler damper climate than at present may account for this phenomenon.

The delicately marked Numbat has a voracious appetite and dentition to match. It feeds almost exclusively on ants and termites, consuming as many as 15,000 daily. The insects are captured on the long sticky tongue and crushed between the batteries of 50 teeth before being swallowed. Dolphins are the only mammals to have more teeth. The numbat is a native of Western Australian forests where it is sometimes captured to be made into a pet.

The marsupial rat or Phascogale is an attractive animal with its large, bushy tail. Found throughout the Australian continent, the phascogale is a powerful gnawer and feeds on a mixed diet similar to that of true rats.

Much the most voracious of the marsupial hunters is the aptly named Tasmanian Devil which gained its name from early European settlers who encountered its savage disposition. The Devil was famous for entering chicken coops and killing far beyond its needs and was known to take sheep. By the 1920s the devil had been exterminated from many areas and was close to extinction. Vigorous controls on hunting, however, have ensured the survival of this hunter. The only marsupial hunter larger than the devil was the Tasmanian Wolf, also considered vermin by the early settlers whose stock it killed. It was slaughtered in large numbers and was generally considered extinct by the 1950s, but recent photographs taken in a remote region appear to show living Tasmanian wolves.

1: Yellow-footed Rock Wallaby.
2: Red Kangaroo (2).
3: Tasmanian Devil.
4: Hairy-nosed Wombat.
5: Numbat.
6: Red-legged Pademelon.
7: Quokka.
8: Brush-tailed Phascogale.

Left: A red kangaroo drinking at an outback waterhole or billabong. This species frequents the arid grasslands of the interior and is capable of travelling many miles from its feeding ground to find a source of water.

INSECTIVORES
The Smallest Mammals

The insect eating mammals live on every continent, except Australia, and are extremely successful in their way of life. They are all small, active creatures. Indeed, the smallest land mammal is the Pygmy White-Toothed Shrew which is less than 1¾ inches (45 mm) in length and weighs one tenth of an ounce (2 g).

Insectivores belong to the group of higher or placental mammals to which the vast majority of mammalian species, including man, belong. Unlike the egg-laying monotremes and pouched marsupials, female placentals carry the young within their bodies until they reach an advanced stage of development. The key to this ability is the placenta, an organ which allows nutrients to pass between the mother and the unborn young without the blood systems of the two mingling. This method is far more efficient than those of the monotremes and marsupials and has given the placentals a decided advantage in evolutionary terms. Wherever placental mammals occur, other forms have been pushed into extinction or into specialised lifestyles

In some ways the insectivores are rather primitive placental mammals. They are small creatures with plantigrade feet bearing five digits, a feature of early mammal species. Taken as a whole the typical insectivore body is very similar to that of the earliest mammals of 100 million years ago.

The one area in which insectivores show great evolutionary change is in their dentition. Insectivore teeth have developed specially to cope with the animals on which they prey. Insects are small creatures encased in a tough exoskeleton of chiton. The insectivores need to be able to catch the insects and to bite through the hard armour. They have therefore developed powerful jaws equipped with small, sharp teeth which neither grind nor crush. They simply impale the insect, crunching its outer shell prior to swallowing.

The largest insectivore is the common tenrec of Madagascar, an island where several primitive mammals have flourished free from competition by more advanced creatures. Growing to around 16 inches (40 cm) the common tenrec is kept by locals as a domestic animal which ends its days as a tasty delicacy. Like many insectivores it is nocturnal and hibernates through inhospitable weather. Due to the fact that it forms part of the diet of many larger mammals, the common tenrec needs to breed prolifically. Over twenty young are born at a time, and each has its own teat.

Only slightly smaller are the solenodons of the West Indies. There are two species of this creature, each restricted to a particular island, one on Cuba the other on Hispaniola. Reaching nearly 2 feet (60 cm) in length the solenodons hunt not only insects but also worms and small reptiles. Unlike the majority of insectivores, the solenodons include a large amount of fruit in their diet.

One of the most successful families in the group is that of the hedgehogs, of which the European hedgehog is the best known. Hedgehogs hide in leaf litter during daylight hours and have a wideranging diet. One feature of their feeding habits is that they readily attack the poisonous adder. Hedgehogs are immune to the venom of this snake and have been known to kill the snake on frequent occasions. The long-eared hedgehog is a desert species of

Above: An East African hedgehog in Nairobi, Kenya. Like other hedgehogs this species feeds on invertebrates which it hunts on nocturnal forays. Left: Elephant shrew perched on a dead tree on arid grassland in Namibia's Etosha National Park.

North Africa. The spines which protect these creatures from attack are modified hairs. When threatened the hedgehog rolls up into a ball which is virtually invulnerable to attack.

More restricted in diet are the moles. The common mole feeds on earthworms and other subterranean invertebrates. To find these the mole digs extensive tunnels beneath the soil. Any small creature which stumbles into these passages is doomed, for it will quickly be snapped up by the patrolling mole. The mole is one of the most voracious of mammals, eating huge amounts of prey and attacking other moles on sight. Only during the breeding season are moles found together.

The body of the mole is superbly adapted to burrowing. It is cylindrical and bears powerful, spade-shaped limbs able to shift large amounts of soil. An energetic mole can construct 50 yards (45 metres) of tunnel in an hour, though such speeds are rarely maintained. The golden mole is not closely related, but shares the mole's lifestyle and its bodily adaptations.

The Pyrennean desman is specialised to an aquatic life, living along river banks in the mountains of southern France. Similarly restricted in distribution is the solenodon of the West Indies. This large insectivore, of which there are two species, is untypical in that it will eat fruit and leaves as well as invertebrates.

The shrews are perhaps the most typical insectivores. The 170 species are solitary animals which prey on various invertebrates. The common shrew is found throughout Europe and northern Asia, but does not hibernate in winter, remaining an active and ferocious hunter throughout the year.

1: Least Shrew.
2: Hispaniolan Solenodon.
3: Forest Elephant Shrew.
4: Pyrenean Desman.
5: Hedgehog.
6: Mole.

BATS
The Night Fliers

The only mammals able to fly are the bats, other 'flying mammals' are merely gliders unable to power themselves through the air. The bats have achieved this remarkable gift by evolving wings capable of bearing their weight. Unlike birds' wings, which are made up of strong feathers, bat wings are formed of skin stretched between elongated fingers. The main wing is formed of tough leathery skin reaching from the lengthened second finger back to the leg and strengthened by other fingers. Stretched between the legs and tail is a further wing membrane of varying size and importance.

It is not clear how bats evolved for the earliest known ancestor of modern bats is *Icaronycteris*, a perfectly formed bat which lived 50 million years ago. It is generally assumed that bats evolved from small, tree-living creatures which evolved the ability to glide from tree to tree to escape predators. The flaps of skin developed for gliding were later adapted to free flight.

The hugely expanded skin area which the evolution of the wing involved brought problems for bats. The increased area meant that more body heat was lost, particularly as the wings were being continually pushed through air cooler than body temperature. Bats have solved this problem by consuming enormous amounts of food which are readily transformed into energy. Bats also need to drink large quantities to make up for evaporation of body fluids through the naked wings.

Modern bats fall into two broad groups which, though they share the power of flight, are very different. The Fruit Bats inhabit the tropical and subtropical areas of the world and, as their name suggests, feed chiefly on fruit. They fly mainly during the day, relying on sight to find their way to heavily-laden fruit trees. When feeding, the bats bite pieces of fruit, and crush them to remove the juice before discarding the flesh and seeds. Only the flesh of the softest, most succulent fruits is eaten.

Fruit bats tend to be large, the Kalong of the Philippines has a wingspan of around 5 feet (1.5 metres) and is sometimes called a flying fox because of its face. The curious hammerhead bat of West Africa is rather smaller, but much noisier. Its raucous cry is a common sound in the rainforest.

Much more numerous and more varied are the insectivorous bats, most of which hunt on the wing. These bats have remarkably grotesque faces, which are in fact specialised adaptations to their nocturnal habits. Flying at night is a dangerous activity, as many wartime

pilots discovered. Not only is the flier liable to collide with others, but landing is a remarkably difficult operation. Bats have evolved a magnificent new sense to help them cope with the problems of flying in the dark.

The new sense is a form of radar, or echo location which is highly sensitive and can detect small, fast-moving objects. When in flight the bat emits burst of ultrasonics up to 60 times per second. The ultrasonic waves are reflected by objects and returned to the bat. The direction and time delay of these reflections allows the bat to build up an accurate picture of its surroundings. It can therefore navigate confidently through the air, avoiding obstructions. When landing, echo location is used to identify a suitable resting place.

When hunting insects, the bat steps up its emission of ultrasound considerably. As it closes on the insect, the bat's ultrasonics are boosted as the hunter attempts to locate its prey precisely and decides on the best angle of attack. Many species scoop up the prey in the flap of wing between their legs and tail before it is transferred to the mouth. A few species of night-flying insects counter bat attacks by an habitual tumbling flight which is carried out at random and which the bat cannot predict.

The adaptations for this echo-location sense are clearly seen in the long-eared bat which has particularly enlarged ears, with special flaps to direct the sound waves into the funnel-shaped organs. It is found throughout northern Europe and Asia, hibernating through the winter. The noctule bat has a similar range but feeds on ground insects, such as beetles. The aptly named red bat of North America migrate hundreds of miles each autumn to avoid the severe cold of Canadian winters.

The face of the lesser horseshoe bat is rather untypical for it emits its ultrasonic not through the mouth, but the nose. The nasal passages are surrounded by a horseshoe shaped fleshy lobes which act as a megaphone, directing the sound in specific directions.

The mexican fishing bat has a well-developed echo location system, though exactly how this helps it to hunt fish is not clear for the water surface would disrupt the sound waves. The system clearly works, however, for the bat swoops low over the sea, plucking prey from the water with great accuracy.

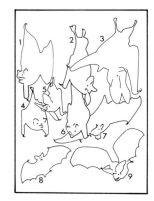

1: Red Bat.
2: Mexican Fishing Bat.
3: African Yellow-winged Bat.
4: Noctule Bat
5: Long-eared Bat
6: Hoary Bat.
7: Horse or Hammer-headed Bat.
8: Lesser Horseshoe Bat.
9: Spotted Bat.

Above: A roosting long-eared bat. Above left: A horseshoe bat hibernating in the New Territories of Hong Kong. Bats wrap their wings around their bodies to help conserve body heat while hibernating.

BUSHBABIES
Wide Eyed Primates

Despite the fact that the primates have produced the most intelligent mammal on earth, namely the human being, they are considered by zoologists to be a rather primitive group. This is due to the number of unspecialised features which have been retained within the primate body. The most notable of these are the plantigrade, or flat, foot; the five digits on each limb and the retention of the clavicle or collar bone. All the more highly developed mammals have lost these features, and most have a reduced number of teeth.

The primates do, however, show a number of specialisations most of which are related to life in the trees. The eyes face forwards giving binocular vision. This allows the primates to judge distance accurately, a vital ability when moving from branch to branch. The fore limb has been adapted into a gripping hand, often with an opposable thumb. This provides a firmer hold on thin twigs and branches. The primates also share the characteristically large brain. This helps them to find food in their chosen habitats.

In the lower primates, the so-called pro-simians, these features are poorly developed. The pro-simians, or 'before monkeys' appeared tens of millions of years ago and formed the base stock from which monkeys and apes evolved. The more advanced primates have driven the pro-simians out of most of their habitats. Modern pro-simians are restricted either to islands or to nocturnal activities.

The lorises inhabit India, Ceylon and neighbouring

areas of southern Asia. They are nocturnal, slow-moving animals which creep cautiously through the dense forests in search of their insect prey. When it nears a victim the loris will lose its lazy motion. Locating the prey with quick, sure fingers, the loris will snatch its victim and gulp it down.

The more elegant species is the slender loris which is especially common in Sri Lanka but is also found in the forests of southern India. Its long, spindly legs and soft grey fur make this animal instantly recognisable beside its larger, stockier relative the slow loris. The slow loris is found throughout southeast Asia from India to Java, but it is rarely seen for it inhabits the densest rain forest and moves cautiously in order to avoid notice.

The closely related potto of West Africa has the tail which the lorises lack but leads a very similar life. As dawn breaks it finds a secluded spot in which to doze away the heat of day until the gathering gloom makes it safe to move again. Its wide-ranging diet takes in leaves,

fruits and various invertebrates. The golden potto inhabits a similarly forested habitat and shares many features with its close relative.

Grouped in the same taxonomic family as the pottos and lorises are the galagos, recently renamed the bushbabies. There are several species of bushbaby of which the needle-clawed bushbaby and the lesser bushbaby are the most appealing. They have small bodies, large heads and enormous eyes. One observer described the eyes as 'quite translucent, marked with minute dividing lines like the grain in an agate - a truly exquisite object.' The beautiful eyes are adaptations to the nocturnal lifestyle, for larger eyes allow in more light to enable the little creature to see better in the deep darkness of the tropical forests.

Bushbabies are agile and active hunters in forests. They scamper through the trees, using their powerful hands to grasp branches and their long tails as balances when leaping across voids to fresh trees. They prey on almost any animal small enough to be subdued, including insects, scorpions and lizards, though they will take fruits and buds when available. When captured by humans, the bushbabies show absolutely no inclination to escape.

Indeed, they will grip an arm as if it were a branch and hold on determinedly. Even mothers with young show no fear of humans.

The Philippines tarsier is, if any thing, more appealing than the bushbabies. Its small, rounded face is dominated by a huge pair of circular eyes, glowing with a warm orange tinge. The tarsier is, however, anything but appealing to the various forest invertebrates which it hunts.

The creature is specially adapted for leaping, and is often considered to be the most adept arboreal leaper in the world. It can launch itself from one branch to hurtle through the black night to land accurately on a slender branch some distance away. Such leaping is powered by the unusually long hind legs with specially lengthened tarsus bones which have given the creature its name. The short front legs are strong and muscular to absorb the impact of landing. All the digits are slender and splayed, ending in rounded pads which increase gripping ability.

1: Needle-clawed Bushbaby.
2: Slender Loris.
3: Philippines Tarsier.
4: Thick-tailed Bushbaby.
5: Golden Potto.
6: Lesser Bushbaby.
7: Slow Loris.
8: Potto.

Left and far left: Lesser bushbabies in the Etosha National Park of Namibia. These attractive little creatures inhabit drier forests in Africa between the Sahara and the open veldt of South Africa.

LEMURS
The Ghosts

In the native tongue of Madagascar *lemur* means 'ghost' and the creatures are often shunned. Active mainly at night the lemurs have the disquieting habit of rushing through trees, rustling the foliage but remaining unseen. Madagascans ascribe similar behaviour to the spirits of the dead, hence the popular name for these harmless and charming primates.

The lemurs are generally lumped together with the bushbabies and pottos as pro-simians, although they form a distinct and numerous subgroup within this category of primates. A characteristic feature of the lemurs is the long, pointed muzzle which all species have and which is covered in short fur. The rest of the body has a dense covering of soft, woolly hair which may feature bold markings. The small head is characterised by extremely large, but dull eyes. Though initially appealing to humans, the lemur eyes register no emotion and soon lose their attraction. Unlike the higher primates, the lemur face is likewise lacking in emotion for it lacks the complicated network of muscles which enables the complex signalling of emotion common to apes.

To further distinguish them from other primates, the lemurs have a quite unique dentition. The 36 teeth are arranged in a jaw which is rather longer in proportion to width than in most primates. The incisors and canines are separated from other teeth by a short gap and project forwards. This enables the lemur to nibble the skin from fruit or to strip trees of bark. Most lemurs have a diet composed chiefly of fruit, although some species take large number of insects and some of the bigger varieties actively hunt small birds and lizards.

Despite these differences the lemurs are true primates. Their lack-lustre eyes are forward which gives them perfect binocular vision. The thumbs and great toes of the feet are fully opposable, enabling the creatures to take a firm grip on branches. Both features help the lemurs to move through the trees. The opposable digits provide a secure grip while the binocular vision allows the creature to judge accurately the distance to the next foothold. The leaping lemurs move by jumping from one vertical trunk to the next rather than by running along branches. On the ground the leaping lemurs adopt a two-legged stance.

The family came into being some time around 60 million years ago and is thus one of the oldest mammalian families to survive to the present day. For many millions of years the lemurs were spread across much of the world, apparently filling the same niche as modern monkeys and evolving a similarly diverse range of species. However, the appearance of the more evolutionarily advanced monkeys drove the lemurs to extinction throughout most of the world. Only on the island of Madagascar did the lemurs survive. Madagascar had been joined to Africa for many millions of years but some time before the evolution of the monkeys it became separated. Isolated on the island the lemurs could continue to exist free from the competition of the higher primates.

Madagascar is a large island which extends through 13 degrees of latitude and has a climate dominated by rain-laden winds sweeping in from the Indian Ocean. This has given rise to a number of different habitats. Along the east coast is a thick belt of rain forest supplied by the waters of the Indian Ocean. West of the central uplands are large deciduous forests while the southern tip is covered by desert and scrub. Much of this natural vegetation has been swept away by the growing human population of the island, but enough remains to support the native wildlife.

The twenty types of lemur have evolved to suit this unique island environment, with certain species being suited to individual habitats. The brown mouse lemur lives in the eastern rainforests while the grey mouse lemur is more at home in the deciduous western forests. The ring-tailed lemur, possibly the most famous species, is a creature of the southern scrublands, though it is often encountered in the deciduous woodlands as well.

Though it is active during daylight hours rather more than most lemurs, the ring-tailed is in many ways typical of its family. Its body is about 18 inches in length, though this is outdistanced by a tail which may reach two feet. Many lemurs have proportionally outsize tails, though the indri has a tail only one inch in length which is covered by its fur. The ring-tailed lemur moves through the woodland in large troops of two or three dozen individuals, dominated by senior females. Each troop has its own feeding territory which it defends against others, though itinerant males are tolerated.

Perhaps because of their diurnal habits the ring-tailed lemurs have long been domesticated as pets. They take readily to human habitations and seem to become attached to their owners, perhaps due to their social habits. Though they usually move on all fours, pet lemurs climb stairs by leaping from one to the next on their hind feet with the tail held vertically. Individuals tend to be playful and inquisitive, being likened to young kittens by European visitors to Madagascan households hosting a pet lemur.

1: Aye-aye.
2: Coquerel's Mouse Lemur.
3: Ring-tailed Lemur.
4: Verreaux's Sifaka (2).
5: Black Lemur.
6: Ruffed Lemur.

Left: A ruffed lemur, also seen with white or brown fur mixed with the black. The species is almost totally arboreal, feeding at dusk on fruits and shoots.

NEW WORLD MONKEYS
Climbing with the Tail

The monkeys fall into two large families both of which contain a number of species, and both of which are restricted geographically. The New World Monkeys inhabit the dense forests of Central and South America. They can easily be distinguished from Old World Monkeys by their fur which is generally thick and woolly. The nostrils of the New World Monkeys are equally distinctive being round and opening sideways, rather than forwards. As a rule they also have long prehensile tails which act as 'fifth hands' when climbing. The hands, in contrast, sometimes lack the opposable thumb and so are only of limited use when climbing.

In past generations the New World Monkeys were particularly favoured as pets. Sailors and travellers often brought a member of one of the smaller species home to delight the children and neighbours. The white cheeked capuchin was one of the favourite species for this purpose. It is almost insatiably curious, picking up objects and playing with them endlessly. Easily distracted, the monkeys would scamper around throughout the day as they investigated their surroundings, time and time again. One individual was trained to run up the curtains, catch flies and to turn the pages of a book as if reading.

In their native forests, however, the capuchin is far from loved. It's natural diet is made up of insects, lizards and birds in addition to various shoots and fruits. The intelligent capuchins quite happily extend their diet to include domestic chickens and crops and are, therefore, unwelcome visitors to human villages.

The closely related squirrel monkey is one of the more visually attractive monkeys. Its quaint, rounded face and disproportionately long tail combine to make it appealing. The long tail is less muscular than that of most New World Monkeys and tends to trail behind the monkey as it scampers through the upper branches of the Amazonian rainforest.

Perhaps the most impressive feature of the monkey is its brain, which is larger in proportion to its body than that of a human. As might be expected the creature leads a highly social life, moving through the forests in bands of 30 or so individuals. When rushing through the virgin forest, the squirrel monkeys prey on small reptiles and birds together with invertebrates and any succulent vegetable matter they come across. However, when a troop comes across a cultivated break in the natural forest they concentrate on vegetable foods. A large troop is capable of stripping fields of fruit in a short period of time and have ruined other crops by devouring tender young shoots at the start of the growing season.

By far the noisiest New World Monkeys are the aptly named howlers of which the red howler is the largest and loudest. The characteristic howling can be heard nearly two miles away and is almost certainly a territorial call. Red howlers live together in family groups of up to ten individuals led by a large, old male. It is only adult males which have the howling ability and they use it to reinforce their social role and territory. The extraordinarily loud call is amplified by a large hollow bone in the larynx which acts as sounding board. The vocal cords are considerably enlarged and the whole apparatus encased in large pocket beneath the lower jaw. The bulging pocket is cloaked by a large beard of dense fur. When calling, the

Left: A white-faced saki sits disconsolately on a branch in the rain forest. The majority of sakis and other New World monkeys are confined to the rainforest, rarely venturing into open country.

male gapes, dropping its lower jaw down and pushing the air out of its lungs rapidly to produce the resonant howling.

Like most of the larger monkeys in South America, the red howler is almost exclusively vegetarian. It feeds on leaves and fruits which appear year round in the lush rainforest.

Perhaps the ugliest monkey to human eyes is the bald uakari of the upper Amazonian Basin. It is covered in long, grey or reddish hair and has a startling bare face and head of red skin which contrasts starkly with its fur. The uakari tends to keep to the highest branches where it searches for succulent fruits or shoots. Rather more attractive is the pale faced saki with its luxuriant fur and characteristic face markings.

The humboldt's woolly monkey is one of the best and most agile climbers in the South American forests. Its fore limbs are longer than the hind limbs, while its tail is extremely long and muscular. It can scamper through the upper branches at speed, calling and chattering to its troop mates. Unlike some other New World Monkeys, the woolly monkeys often come to the ground in the search for food.

One of the most extraordinary New World Monkeys may still be awaiting discovery. In 1917 the naturalist Francois de Loys shot a creature in the Venezuelan forests which stood 5 feet (1.6 metres) tall and lacked a tail. De Loys measured and photographed the creature which he thought to be an ape. Sceptical scientists dismissed the photograph as 'dubious' though for no good reason and declared that since no apes were known to live in South America the story was obviously confused. More open minded scientists felt that the creature may have been a type of tailless monkey. No second specimen of this remarkable creature has ever been sighted so its classification remains uncertain.

1: *White-faced Saki.*
2: *Common Squirrel Monkey.*
3: *Red Howler Monkey.*
4: *White-cheeked Capuchin.*
5: *Bald Uakari.*
6: *Humboldt's Woolly Monkey.*

OLD WORLD MONKEYS
The Dog Faced Primates

The majority of Old World Monkeys are tree-living species which forage through the forests of Africa and Asia in search of food. They are generally reckoned to be more intelligent than the New World Monkeys, though this is not the chief distinguishing feature.

Most noticeable is the fact that the nostrils of Old World Monkeys are set close together and face down, rather than outwards. Their fur is hairy, rather than woolly and although their tails are often long they are not prehensile and are of limited use when climbing.

One of the most beautiful of these creatures is the guereza colobus. Covered with short black hair, the monkey is distinguished by the long, silky white fur which cascades from its flanks and forms a great tassel at the end of its tail. The beauty of this creature is such that it was hunted for its fur for many years and in the late 1970s it appeared to be facing extinction. Recent control measures seem to give this monkey a secure future.

Like all colobuses, the guereza spends virtually its entire life in the highest forest branches. It feeds on the leaves and fruits of the tropical forests, moving noisily through the foliage in large family groups.

Equally striking in appearance is the proboscis monkey or kahau of Borneo. The adult males grow huge, bulbous noses from which the species takes its name. It seems that the nose is used when calling, for the honk of a male proboscis can be heard over great distances.

Inhabiting the dense foliage of the mangrove swamps off the Borneo coast, the proboscis monkeys feed on leaves and fruits. These are chiefly of the stunted mangrove trees amongst which they live, but the monkeys seem equally willing to feed on other plants when they are to hand.

The guenon monkeys have amongst their numbers two remarkable animals, the brightly marked moustached Monkey of the Congo and the less striking patas monkey which inhabits open plains and scrubland in East Africa. Like baboons, the patas lives in large troops and spends much of its time on the ground. It feeds on small creatures, insects and seeds, manipulating its small food with delicate hands.

It also shares the problem of baboons that it cannot hide from enemies on the grasslands. While baboons became large enough to fight off predators, the patas evolved the ability to run. It is easily the fastest primate, reaching speeds of over 30 miles per hour (50 kilometres per hour) in short dashes.

Inhabiting the open plains and forests of Africa are the baboons, or dog-faced monkeys, the most distinctive of all Old World Monkeys. Found throughout sub-Saharan Africa, the baboons are highly social animals living in troops of anything from 20 to 200 individuals. Most of the troop comprises females and youngsters who are led and protected by one or more old males.

Unlike most monkeys the baboons live on the ground, though some may seek the safety of trees at night. They move on all fours, squatting on their haunches to feed. most species are omnivorous, taking insects and small vertebrates with as much relish as they pick fruit and vegetation. Some farmers regard baboons as beneficial for they keep down various pests, but others consider them pests themselves when they steal crops.

Above: A troop of colobus monkeys near Naivasha in Kenya. This species is notable for the fact that evolution has virtually destroyed the thumb and the front limbs now carry only four digits.

The opportunistic feeding habits of the baboons often bring them close to humans for settlements provide much in the way of food scraps. One golfer on a South African link suddenly found himself surrounded by over 100 baboons, who sat down and watched him. The golfer beat a hasty and wise retreat for baboons are powerful animals, especially when acting together, and are able to drive off lions with ease. Equipped with strong arms and ferociously sharp canines, baboons are formidable animals. They have often been reported to carry of human infants as prey, and have even attacked adults on occasion.

The social structure of the baboons is remarkably complex, and seems to be largely developed to combat the dangers of life in the open. Most primate species hide from danger in dense foliage, but no such safety is open to baboons. They move and feed in plain view of predators. While the majority of the troop is feeding, individuals will keep watch for any approaching danger often posting themselves some distance from the troop. At the first sign of attack the alarm is given and the troop concentrates and moves on. The social hierarchy of baboons provides for guards, sentinels and fighters.

The largest of the baboons is the Mandrill, found in the forests of West Africa. This creature feeds on a varied diet of small forest animals and many sorts of fruits and nuts. Its most distinctive feature is its snout. Like that of all baboons it is long and blunt, carrying the nostrils at its end. But it is the coloration which allowed one 19th century traveller to describe the mandrill as a 'grotesque mixture of fantastic embellishments and repulsive ferocity'. The striking and curious ridged red and blue markings appear to be sexual signalling devices. Only the male sports them and the startling contrast seems to be attractive to the dull-coloured females.

1: Moustached Monkey.
2: Colobus Monkey.
3: Proboscis Monkey.
4: Mandrill.
5: Patas Monkey.

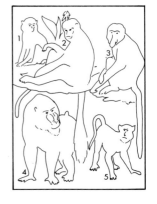

APES
Man-like Primates

The apes are the closest living relatives of human beings. Quite how close the relationship is has long been a source of controversy in scientific circles. Ever since Charles Darwin first suggested the close connection between humans and apes there has been disagreement. The latest argument is between those scientists who study fossils and those who investigate genetics. The two disciplines give very different dates for the time when human ancestors diverged from ape ancestors. The difference between the estimates being as much as 10 million years.

Whatever the point of divergence of groups within the ape family, the history of the apes themselves is fairly well known. The oldest fossil apes have been found in Africa and date back around 35 million years. These early apes adapted themselves to a forest lifestyle in the dense jungles of central Africa. Around 20 million years ago Africa became joined to Eurasia, allowing the apes to spread out to colonise the forests of southern Asia. Ultimately humans would learn to use fire and clothing and so were able to inhabit more inhospitable climates. The non-human apes, however, remained tied to their warm forests.

Four distinct groups of ape, including just ten species, exist today, with two groups in Asia and two more in Africa. Although there are distinct differences between the groups, they all share several features in common. In addition to the general primate characteristics of binocular vision and opposable digits, the apes have a more upright posture than other primates, tending to move or rest with the back held vertically rather than horizontally. All apes lack a tail, having merely three or four tail bones which are not visible externally and which are often fused to form a solid coccyx.

Apes have fairly consistent breeding habits, which are characterised by long periods of time. Gestation takes several months in all species, approaching ten months in the larger species, and is followed by a lactation period at least as long. Usually only one young is born, although twins may occur. In most species the infant is entirely dependent on its mother for several years, and often remains socially attached for some years after it becomes able to fend for itself.

The smallest apes are the gibbons which inhabit the forests of southeast Asia. Rarely more than three feet tall, the gibbons have become specialised to moving through the trees, an adaptation seen most clearly in their front limbs. Their arms have become elongated to such an extent that when standing upright the knuckles reach the ground. The hands are likewise rather long and the fingers curve sharply inwards, forming strong hooks.

The gibbon uses these to swing from branch to branch with effortless grace. It will even launch itself through the air to grasp a branch several feet away. The leaping ability of the gibbons is almost legendary, with some observers claiming the apes can change direction in mid air. Using these remarkable limbs, gibbons can move swiftly through the upper branches and canopy of their forest homes. On the rare occasions when they do come to the ground, gibbons walk on their hind feet and use their arms to balance themselves, rather as a tightrope walker uses a pole.

Sharing part of the range of the gibbons is the orang-utan of Sumatra and Borneo, of which there is only one species. Known to locals as 'the old man of the forest' the orang-utan may have a surprisingly human appearance with its flat face and conspicuous beard. Like gibbons, the orang-utan feeds chiefly on fruit though it will take birds and eggs and lives in dense forests. Its method of movement is however very different. In place of spectacular leaps and swinging rushes, the orang-utan moves slowly, walking on top of larger branches and hanging from more slender boughs. It is found on the forest floor more often than the gibbon.

The two types of African ape are the chimpanzee and the gorilla. The chimpanzee is the smaller and more common, reaching a height of five feet and being found in large troops in the forests of central Africa. These gregarious apes are intelligent and display a wide diversity of habits especially when procuring food. They feed chiefly on fruit and leaves, but will eat insects and young birds eagerly. Some have been observed hunting small mammals and lizards. They feed during the day, lying up at night, and will happily use twigs and stones as tools in food gathering.

Larger than the chimpanzee is the gorilla, the heavyweight among primates. Standing taller than the average human, the gorilla is thickset and muscular and may top the scales at 500 lbs. In the past local tribesmen ascribed almost supernatural strength to the gorilla, alleging that it could drive off lions with ease, killed leopards out of hand and was prone to carrying off human women to its forest home. Such tales have long been discredited, but the gorilla is an enormously powerful animal which can be exceptionally dangerous when it feels threatened. As with all the larger apes, the gorilla has become increasingly rare in recent years due to hunting and destruction of habitat. Determined efforts may be required to save these animals.

1: *White-handed Gibbon.*
2: *Orang-utan.*
3: *Siamang.*
4: *Gorilla.*
5: *Chimpanzee.*

Left: A juvenile orang-utan. Such young apes more normally cling to their mother's fur as she moves through the trees in search of fruit and seeds. Young may be suckled for several years, though they take an increasingly solid diet after two years.

ANTEATERS AND PANGOLINS
Toothless Mammals

Some mammals are opportunists, able to feed on a variety of foods in a number of habitats, but others have become specialists, none more so than the anteaters. The present species are the result of a long evolutionary trail which took place in South America, where most still live.

For many millions of years the continent was cut off from other lands and pursued its own mammalian evolution. As in Australia, marsupials played a prominent part as the major predators. Some placental mammals were present, and these took over the role of herbivores. Though they evolved into a wide variety of forms, some as large as an elephant, the placental mammals retained many primitive features.

When the two Americas joined some time around one million years ago the faunas of the two continents mixed. For the most part the creatures of South America came off worst. The large marsupial hunters were quickly driven to extinction while the primitive placentals were replaced by more advanced creatures from the north. Only specialists, such as the anteaters, which enjoyed a great advantage over less adapted animals, managed to survive. The evolutionary price paid for this competitiveness is that the anteaters have become unable to pursue any other way of life. If the ants were ever to disappear for any reason, the anteaters would simply starve into extinction.

The giant anteater is the most curious of the entire group and lives up to its name by being the largest as well. The total length of this creature is around 7 feet (2.1 metres), of which nearly half is made up of the large bushy tail. The extraordinary tail has two uses. The more critical is to balance the weight of the body when the creature rears on to its hind legs to feed, but it is also useful when resting. The tail is lifted up to cover the body, shading the animal from the heat of the day. The long, coarse hairs of the tail camouflage the sleeping animal, giving it the appearance of a pile of dried grass.

When on the move, the anteater walks on the soles of its hind feet, but on the knuckles of its forefeet. The 'hands' are turned inwards to keep the long, sharp claws off the ground. The claws are not only useful weapons if attacked, but are also of vital importance to the anteater's lifestyle. When the creature finds an ant or termite nest it attacks the rock-hard mud with its powerful claws. After much digging, the anteater tears out great lumps of nest, clearing a path into the interior.

The ants immediately scurry out to discover the cause of the damage to their nest and to repair it. But the anteater is waiting, flicking its long tongue in and out with rapid motion. The tongue stretches more than 2 feet (60 centimetres) out of the mouth and is covered in thick, sticky saliva. Any ants touched by the tongue are trapped and brought back into the anteater's mouth. There they are swallowed and the tongue pushed out to whisk again through the internal tunnels of the ant nest. A giant anteater may spend long periods clawing at a nest, digging through to the nursery chambers where the succulent larvae are kept. Thousands of ants may be consumed before the anteater moves on.

The more lightly built tamandua or tree anteater is about half the length of the giant anteater and is found in more densely wooded country. It lives in the dense foliage and hunts mainly at night. It will tear open the nests which some ant species build in tree branches, using its prehensile tail to secure itself while the front limbs are engaged. Like its giant cousin, the tamandua has a long, sticky tongue which it flicks quickly through the internal passages of the ant nest to capture as many insects as possible. If danger threatens, the tamandua will attempt either to hide or escape. When cornered, the tamandua may strike with its claws, or may lunge forward and hug its attacker.

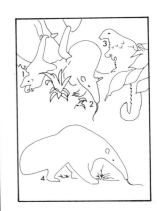

1: Silky, or Two-toed Anteater.
2: Tamandua or Collared Anteater.
3: African Tree Pangolin.
4: Giant Anteater.

Smaller still is the aptly named pygmy anteater which ranges throughout the dense forests of Central and South America. It is rarely seen not only because of its small size, but also because it is active only at night.

Similar in many ways to the anteaters is the giant pangolin which can be seen as the African equivalent of the American anteaters, though it is unrelated. It is likewise equipped with powerful front claws to tear open termite nests and with a long, sticky tongue to collect insects. The most obvious difference between the two is the tough body armour of the pangolins. The scales are greatly modified hairs which overlap each other and have sharp, pointed ends. Faced with danger, a pangolin will either retreat to its burrow or roll itself into a ball which is virtually impervious to attack.

Above: A female tamandua tearing open a tree-termite nest to reach the insects within while the young anteater clings to her fur and watches the progress of the attack. Far left: The striped markings of a mother giant anteater and her young merge perfectly as the baby rides on its mother's back.

THE ARMADILLOS
Armoured Diggers

The armadillos, of which there are about 20 species, are a quite remarkable group of mammals. Indeed they are unique in having a tough bony shell quite unlike that of any other mammal. In many other ways they are distinctive too, and this seems to be due to their long history of evolutionary isolation.

Some 80 million years ago South America became separated from all other continents, an isolation not broken until around 1 million years ago. During that time the mammals of South America evolved into many unique forms. Some were parallels of other creatures evolving elsewhere but some, like the armadillos, were unique. The armadillo line reached its apogee with the glyptodonts, massive lumbering animals the largest of which was as bulky as an ox and had a long tail armed with a spiky knob which could be swung as an effective defensive weapon. When South America joined North America, many southern mammalian groups became extinct, but not the armadillos. They were so well adapted to their way of life that no newcomer could supplant them. Indeed, some species of armadillo invaded the northern continent and have become common throughout Central America.

The distinctive armour of the armadillos is unique in that it is based upon bony plates, a feature found in many reptiles but in no other mammals. The small bony nodules are set deep in the skin and act as roots for tough horny sheaths, which form the visible armour. On the top of the head the horny plates are fused together to form a solid shield. The same fusing is found over the shoulders and hips, where, large masses of inflexible armour is found.

In order to make movement easier, the central sections of the body are covered by more flexible protection. The horny sheaths here are fused together in a number of bands running around the body. The number of bands varies between species, with the total giving some species their common names. The three-banded armadillo and nine-banded armadillo being cases in point. This centre section allows the armadillo to flex its body when running, attaining greater speed. The armadillos have become famous for their agility and speed, despite their hefty armour plating. Modern researchers in Texas launch night-time armadillo hunts which stretch even the most athletic scientist to the utmost. When an armadillo is caught in the light beam from the research truck, the men leap out and give chase, armed with nets and poles. Very often the armadillo is too quick and gets away.

When flight is not possible, the armadillo resorts to digging for safety. During the day most armadillos rest in permanent burrows, and will dig themselves to safety when threatened. Charles Darwin took a great interest in armadillos during his voyage on the *Beagle*, but complained 'the instant one is perceived, it was necessary, in order to catch it, almost to tumble off one's horse; for in soft soil the animal burrowed so quickly that its hinder quarters would almost disappear before one could alight.'

If the hardness of the soil makes rapid digging impossible, the armadillo will roll itself up into a tight ball. Only the tough armoured shell is presented to the outside world, the vulnerable belly being hidden.

Most armadillos feed on a wide-ranging diet, but their choice of food is limited by their dentition. Though some species may have as many as 100 teeth, the armadillos are counted among the edentates, or toothless mammals. The reason for this is that the teeth are weak and lack enamel. Armadillos can only tackle fairly soft foods. Some species concentrate almost exclusively on invertebrates, though others will dig up roots. The creatures therefore enjoy a mixed reputation among farmers. Some welcome the armadillos' onslaught on insect pests, while others bemoan the nibbled potatoes and roots.

The gauchos of the South American pampas discovered last century that armadillos were not above taking carrion. The gauchos ate large amounts of meat, slaughtering wild cattle when on the grasslands. After butchering the carcass and eating their meals the gauchos noticed that the discarded entrails and offal were surrounded by large numbers of armadillos. The little creatures were attracted by the smell of blood and slowly chewed their way through the mass of soft leftovers.

Other armadillos are more active hunters. One 19th century naturalist found that forest armadillos preyed on eggs, bird hatchlings and small creatures as well as fruits. 'It's method of capturing mice was certainly ingenious,' he wrote. 'It hunted by smell and when nearing it's prey became agitated. The exact spot discovered, the body was raised slowly to a sitting posture and then flung suddenly forwards so that the mouse, or nest of mice, was imprisoned beneath and promptly despatched.' He also saw an armadillo kill a snake by a similar pouncing motion.

Two of the most extraordinary armadillos are the giant armadillo and the fairy armadillo. As its name suggests the giant armadillo is the largest, measuring 5 feet (1.6 metres) in length and weighing as much as an adult human. It is armed with strong front claws with which it will smash open termite nests for food. The much rarer fairy armadillo or pichiciago lives only in the dry, sandy areas of western Argentina. It is a particularly fine burrower, living on worms and insects. it is peculiar in having a circular shield of armour resting vertically over its rear. It is thought that this acts as a plug in the burrow, making the creature safe from attack from behind.

1: *Giant Armadillo (2).*
2: *Three-banded Armadillo.*
3: *Hairy Armadillo.*
4: *Six-banded Armadillo.*
5: *Pichi.*
6: *Naked-tailed Armadillo.*
7: *Nine-banded Armadillo.*
8: *Burmeister's Armadillo.*
9: *Fairy Armadillo.*

Left: A juvenile giant armadillo noses across the pampas. These creatures are found throughout the drier regions of South America from the Caribbean Ocean to the River Plate. It is thought that females give birth to single young, though unconfirmed reports of twins have been made.

SLOTHS
The Slowest Mammals

Grouped with the armadillos and anteaters in the order edentata, the sloths are, like its cousins, restricted to South and Central America. Like the other members of the order, the sloths are highly specialised creatures which have become completely adapted to one particular way of life.

In the case of the sloths this is a life among the forests of northern South America. The sloths move through the foliage searching for leaves on which to feed and hiding from predators. Unlike the other tree-top leaf eaters of the same area, the monkeys, the sloths have developed a remarkably slow pace of life which has become so well known as to make its common name synonymous with laziness and sleepiness.

There are only two species of sloth, but they are so different that most scientists place them in different genera, though within one family. The two species take their names from external features, the larger being the three-toed sloth and the smaller the two-toed sloth, but internal variations are much greater. For example the two-toed sloth has 48 ribs to the three-toed sloth's 30. Both creatures inhabit the same forests of Brazil and Venezuela, though the three-toed sloth is found as far north as Guatemala and the two-toed sloth was placed by some early reports in the West Indies.

The sloths are unique among mammals for their method of movement, and it is around this that their lives are constructed. Unlike monkeys which run along the tops of branches or swing rapidly from bough to bough, the sloths hang underneath branches using all four limbs to secure a hold. The limbs are superbly adapted to such a posture. The legs are long and strong, terminating in elongated and extremely sharp curved claws. There being no need to spread the digits for any reason, these have become joined throughout their length. Only the claws are separated, and these lie flush throughout their length. With these hooked claws, the sloths secure themselves to a branch so tenaciously that it is extremely difficult to dislodge them. Even jaguars have been known to give up the attempt.

Shifting the grip of one limb at a time, the sloths move slowly through the canopy. The exact speed of which a sloth is capable is unknown but bursts of 20 feet (6 metres) per minute might be achieved. A speed of around 10 feet (3 metres) per minute is probably more typical. Not only does the sloth move at a slow speed, but its every movement is cautious and lacking in haste. When it moves is head to reach a new bunch of leaves, it does so with infinitely sluggish motion. But any movement is the exception rather than the rule for the sloth spends most of its time completely immobile. It sleeps for around sixteen hours each day, and rests for a further two. Only the remaining six hours are spent moving and feeding.

One of the benefits of such sluggishness is that it provides the sloth with its most effective form of defence. When hanging motionless beneath a branch the sloth is virtually indistinguishable from the surrounding wood and foliage. The camouflage is helped by the fact that when sleeping the sloth pulls its legs together and tucks its head between its forelimbs. This completely alters its silhouette, making it appear very similar to a mass of hanging moss or a nest of some kind.

The similarity of appearance with vegetation is further enhanced by the long, straggly fur which adorns the creature. Due to its upside down mode of life, the hairs on the sloth fall naturally from its belly to its back, unlike all other mammals where the hair falls the other way. Each individual strand of hair is ridged and grooved in such a fashion as to provide a purchase hold for algae. These microscopic plants infest the fur in vast numbers, colouring it green. When drought strikes the forest, the algae suffers from the lack of moisture as much as the trees so the sloth appears to yellow with the drying vegetation.

The various species of sloth have managed to survive in some numbers, perhaps because of their excellent camouflage and tenacious grip. They have certainly been persecuted by locals for their flesh is highly esteemed. When European travellers first pushed into the forest interior they found that the local tribesmen would eagerly ask them to shoot sloths hanging high in trees. The reason for this was that the impact of a bullet often had the effect of knocking the sloth from its perch to fall to the ground. The traditional weapons of blowdarts and arrows failed to do this and necessitated a stiff scramble through the trees to recover the creature.

In 1900 the sloths created an immense stir in scientific circles when a skull and skin were found in a Patagonian cave. The skull and skin were quite fresh, as if they had been removed from the animal only a short time before. The excitement was caused by the fact that the remains belonged to a form of giant ground sloth standing some 15 feet (5 metres) tall which had been thought to have been extinct for many thousands of years. The following year an expedition set out from Britain with the sole intention of locating what was believed to be an isolated population of these creatures. No giant sloths were found and it was afterwards postulated that the atmospheric conditions of the cave had kept the skin fresh for centuries.

1: Three-toed Sloth (2).
2: Two-toed Sloth.

Left: A two-toed sloth in its natural habitat of trailing leaves and stems. The camouflage effect of the coarse hair, which is the sloth's only protection against predators, can be clearly seen here.

HARES, RABBITS AND PIKAS
The Grazing Pests

For centuries considered a specialised group of rodents, the lagomorphs have now been placed in an order of their own. Many naturalists believe that the lagomorphs are closely related to the rodents. Exactly how close this relationship is, and when the evolutionary lines diverged, remains a matter of debate.

The major difference between the two groups is in the dentition, though it was this very feature which previously grouped the two together. Rodents have a pair of large incisors at the front of their mouths, no canines and varying numbers of molars. The incisors are typically very large and project from the mouth. Lagomorphs share this pattern in all but one feature. Tucked behind the dominant first pair of incisors is a second, smaller pair. Coupled with slight variations in chewing mechanism, these extra teeth have caused the separation of the two groups.

The fifty-four species of lagomorphs can be conveniently divided into three broad groups; the rabbits, the hares and the pikas. Of these the first two are by far the most numerous both in terms of species number and absolute numbers. Indeed the huge breeding potential of these animals ranks among their most distinctive features.

The wild rabbit is one of the most notoriously rapid breeders and has become a major pest in many areas. It feeds chiefly upon grass, consuming vast quantities which humans would rather were used by domestic sheep and cattle. They also strip bark from young trees, rearing on their hind legs to reach higher, apparently in an effort to exercise their teeth rather than to feed. The rabbit's depredations were probably worst in Australia where special conditions came together to create the 'rabbit problem' as it became known.

The first rabbits came out to Australia in 1859, and six were released to provide a familiar source of meat for the European settlers. In Australia the rabbits found an ideal habitat. There was abundant grass for them to feed upon, and an almost total absence of predators. The phenomenal breeding capacity of rabbits took over. An adult female produces four litters of about seven young each year. Young of the first litter are themselves breeding before the fourth is born. In unrestricted breeding a single pair can produce over a million descendants within two years. The rabbits bred prolifically, spreading out to take advantage of new pastures at the rate of 70 miles a year. By the year 1900 rabbits were a major problem, stripping pasture of grass badly needed by sheep and cattle.

Squatters and farmers tried to control the pests by erecting rabbit fences, tall wire barriers which extended deep beneath the ground. These needed constant patrolling by mounted men and were expensive. The answer to the rabbit problem came in 1948 when a virulent virus which affected only rabbits was released at a number of sites. Myxomatosis swept through the rabbit population like wildfire, destroying countless millions of the animals. The disease was later introduced to other nations, to restrict their rabbit populations.

Hares are somewhat less prolific and are not considered to be such a serious pest. Indeed they have needed to be preserved from extinction in some areas where their sporting potential is valued. Hares are extremely fast movers, reaching 45 miles per hour (70 kilometres per hour) over short distances. They are also agile, one hunter was surprised to see a started hare dash straight for a river bank only to jink aside at the last moment. The pursuing greyhound failed to turn in time and plunged headlong into the water.

The common brown hare of Africa, Europe and Asia has been introduced to the New World where it is thriving. During the daylight hours it retreats to a small hollow in the ground, where it crouches for protection. At night it emerges to feed on fruit, fungi, twigs and whatever other vegetable food it can find. Similar in markings is the snowshoe hare, at least during the summer. When winter approaches this inhabitant of northern Canada changes in colour to become buff white. The changing coat colour serves to camouflage the animal in the varying circumstances of the season. A similar seasonal colour change can be seen in the mountain hare. This camouflage adaptation is unusual amongst mammals, though it is common in birds.

Rather different from either rabbits or hares are the pikas, variously known as mouse hares or calling hares. The latter name derives from their habit of standing up and emitting a long, high-pitched call. Pikas resemble small rabbits with short ears. They live in rocky mountainous areas of Asia and North America. One species lives high in the Himalayas, being found at heights approaching 20,000 feet (6,000 metres). Like other lagomorphs, the pikas feed on grass and greenery. They tend to stock up during the summer, laying grass out to dry into hay and storing it in burrows.

1: Brown Hare (2).
2: Mountain Hare (2).
3: Snowshoe Hare.
4: Northern Pika.
5: Black-tailed Jack Rabbit.
6: Rabbit.
7: Red Pika.
8: Steppe Pika.

Above: A group of wild rabbits pause from eating grass to watch an intruder. Left: A pika in Wyoming's Teton National Park.

NEW WORLD RODENTS
American gnawers

The most significant feature of the rodents, indeed that which gave them their name, is their dentition. The teeth of a rodent are utterly unlike those of any other mammal and have determined much rodent behaviour.

The real distinguishing features are the front incisors of which there is one pair in each jaw. These teeth are very powerful and long, with roots reaching back to the rear of the jaws. The base of the root is open to blood vessels, allowing for continual growth throughout the lifetime of the owner. At the feeding end of the teeth, only the front edge is covered by tough enamel. This means that the rear edge wears more quickly resulting in a sharp chisel-shape to the teeth.

In an effort to keep their constantly growing teeth to a manageable size, rodents need to gnaw throughout their adult lives. Most rodents feed on fairly tough food which serves to wear down their incisors, but many cannot rely on food to keep their tooth-growth under control. They resort to gnawing on any convenient object tough enough to wear away the teeth. Some rodents have even been observed gnawing at metal bars.

The consequences of unbridled tooth growth would be very serious. Where accident has removed one tooth, its pair can grow at prodigious speed, having nothing against which to work. In some unfortunate individuals the tooth has grown to such an extent that it projects right out of the mouth and cuts into the face.

One specialised group of rodents to achieve great success in the New World is the porcupine family of which there are several species. These creatures have protection against predators in the form of a mass of sharp quills which cover their bodies. The spines are specially adapted hairs which have become enormously thickened and strengthened. Like hairs, the spines can be raised or lowered by tiny muscles embedded in the skin. When danger threatens, the quills are erected, to form a nearly impenetrable hedge to predators.

The tree porcupine, or South American porcupine as it is otherwise known, lives up to both common names by inhabiting the forests of South America. The spines of this creature are fairly short and are hidden amongst long fur. Its feet are specially adapted to grasping branches while its long tail is strongly prehensile and serves as an additional climbing tool.

The closely related North American porcupine is spread throughout the forests from Alaska to New Mexico and is a fine climber. It lacks the prehensile tail of its South American cousin, however, and relies on its squat limbs for climbing. The spines of this creature are larger and more effective than those of its southern relative. They project beyond the fur and have barbed tips. Once embedded in the flesh of a predator these are remarkably difficult to remove and often cause painful abcesses. Hunters soon learn to treat this porcupine with care.

Even more impressive are the quills of the crested porcupine of Africa. The enormously long spines of this creature are usually laid flat against the fur, but when danger threatens they are erected in a tall crest on the head and an impressive fan reaching backwards from the hind quarters. Faced by a hunter, the crested porcupine will flee, presenting a bristling barrier of tough spines.

Old time tales spoke of porcupines shooting quills at pursuers. In fact, the porcupine's trick is to suddenly stop in flight, back into the pursuer and then run off, leaving quills embedded in its adversary.

The closely related coypu, or swamp beaver, is widespread across much of South America inhabiting rivers and marshy areas. It is active during the day seeking out the plants on which it thrives. Like other rodents, it is an excellent digger excavating long galleries in which to live. Its habit of starting burrows in river banks has caused many to collapse into the stream. Its soft, dense fur has led to the coypu being bred in captivity and raised on fur farms around the world. In many areas individuals have escaped and established breeding colonies in lands far removed from their home territory. In East Anglia a coypu population became a major pest before it was exterminated by vigorous action.

Also highly prized for its fur is the diminutive chinchilla which is native to the rocky uplands of Chile, where its fur protects it from intense cold. The demand for the soft, dense and luxurious fur of this small creature has made it extremely rare in the wild, but the activities of fur farms is reducing the pressure on wild populations.

More familiar as a pet is the guinea pig, the domesticated form of the cavy. Guinea pigs vary greatly in colour and texture of coat and so are grouped into various races.

Related to the guinea pig, but much larger is the capybara, the biggest rodent of all. Reaching over 4 feet (1.3 metres) in length, the capybara swims excellently and feeds on aquatic plants. It is a highly social animal, living in groups of around a dozen which are active chiefly at dusk and dawn.

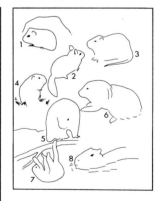

1: Guinea Pig.
2: Chinchilla.
3: Coypu.
4: Guira.
5: North American Porcupine.
6: Crested Porcupine.
7: South American Porcupine.
8: Capybara.

Above: The North American porcupine which climbs in trees to reach shoots, fruits and tender young bark. The needle sharp spines are hidden among the coarse hair and can inflict unpleasant injuries.

SQUIRRELS
Agile Rodents

Squirrels are generally thought of as nimble tree-living rodents which are specialist climbers and leapers of great ability. A large number of squirrels do, indeed follow this lifestyle, but the sub-order of rodents to which the squirrels belong also include a large number of squirrel-like ground dwellers and the beaver.

Two species of squirrel typify the arboreal creature to European and American imaginations. In Europe the red squirrel is the dominant tree-living rodent. It seems to prefer coniferous woodland, but is common in deciduous forests. Wherever it lives, the mammal feeds on seeds and fruits though fungi are also consumed. It is an extremely nimble and fleet-footed creature. Its powerful limbs and long claws make it a wonderful climber which is able to scamper up sheer trunks or along branches at bewildering speed. It is also an accomplished leaper and will readily spring from one bough to another across a yawning gap.

When the warmer weather of spring brings the breeding season the squirrels start building a nest, or drey. This is generally a domed structure woven of twigs, moss and leaves, rather like a bird's nest. In this drey the female gives birth to as many as half a dozen blind and helpless young. Red squirrels are thought to pair for life, and the male plays an active role in caring for the young.

Within a few weeks, the young are able to look after themselves and the pair can produce a second litter. Such a high rate of reproduction is necessary for the squirrels are prey to a large number of predators, including cats and owls. Occasionally a huge population boom takes place, for reasons not yet understood, and the squirrels migrate. Groups of hundreds of creatures gather together in the trees before setting off on journeys which may take them hundreds of miles from home. New areas are colonised, but the majority of migrating squirrels fall prey to hunters and accident. In Eastern Europe such migrating hordes are hunted by humans for their pelts.

In eastern North America the grey squirrel is the most common form, being particularly numerous in the deciduous forests where it finds nuts and bird eggs. It also

has the habit of gnawing the bark off saplings in order to suck the sap. The grey squirrel was introduced to Britain earlier this century, perhaps because of its attractive garden antics. It rapidly drove the red squirrel from most areas and became so destructive in forestry areas that it is now considered a pest and vermin.

Rather larger and most spectacular is the African giant squirrel which is a specialised squirrel highly adapted to a diet of oil-palm seeds. Reaching well over 2 feet (60 cm) in length, this squirrel is rarely seen for it is highly skilled at hiding itself in foliage. Its diet is highly nutritious but deficient in calcium, so the squirrels will often scavenge small bones from predators' kills.

Even more specialised are the flying squirrels of North America and Southeast Asia. These creatures do not actually fly, but are able to glide long distances, taking the leaping abilities of their cousins to an extreme. The gliding is achieved by spreading out a large flap of skin which runs from the ankle of the front leg to that of the hind leg.

Further removed still from the basic squirrel pattern are the ground squirrels, marmots and prairie dogs which make up a large number of species. The ground squirrels are found in many areas and are a major pest for they take large quantities of grain from farmland. They store huge amounts of food against the coming winter, often taking more than they need. The prairie dogs do not hoard food, but otherwise are very similar. They live in large colonies on open land and are a major pest, preferring to nibble growing crops and grass. The marmots are restricted to mountainous areas where they live in small colonies of around a dozen animals.

Though the ground living groups are notable burrowers, the true architects of the rodent world are the beavers. These animals are famous for constructing dams across streams and so creating large artificial ponds. The purpose of the ponds is to create a stable area of open water in which to build a lodge. Constructed, like the dam, of branches, twigs and stones plastered with mud, the lodge contains a living chamber spacious enough for several beavers. Seen from outside, the lodge resembles a mound of wood some 15 feet (5 metres) in diameter, and has no obvious opening. The two entrances lie beneath the surface of the water in order to provide protection against predators. Quantities of timber are stored in the lodge and beneath the surface of the pond to provide secure sources of food during the winter.

All this impressive building work is carried out by the beaver using only its teeth and hands. Fully grown trees may be felled after persistent gnawing of its trunk, and then stripped of branches, twigs and bark by continued gnawing. Long canals may be dug by the beavers in order to float the timber from the felling site to the pond. It is in the water that beavers are at their best for they are superb swimmers. The hind feet are webbed while the tail is shaped like a paddle to power the creature through the water.

The beaver was formerly widely spread across both Europe and North America, but intensive fur trapping has pushed it to extinction in many areas. More recently protective laws have been introduced and the beaver is on the increase in many areas.

1: *Marmot.*
2: *Asiatic Striped Palm Squirrel.*
3: *Ground Squirrel.*
4: *Malabar or Indian Giant Squirrel.*
5: *Red Squirrel.*
6: *Flying Squirrel.*
7: *African Bush Squirrel.*
8: *Beaver.*

Left: A red squirrel on the Isle of Wight, one of the few areas of Britain where this species is still plentiful. The red squirrel is still common throughout mainland Europe and Asia where the American grey squirrel has not been introduced.

RATS AND MICE
The Ancient Pests

Rodents have been considerable pests for as long as humans have been agricultural, settled peoples. The settlements of ancient peoples excavated by archaeologists have been found to contain rodent remains, and prove that early man made considerable efforts to safeguard his grain against rodent attacks.

Perhaps the most formidable rodent pest is the rat which has also proved to be one of the most persistent. One recent study suggested that in any urban society the number of rats is approximately equal to the number of humans, a quite disturbing conclusion.

Rats are omnivorous and great opportunists, taking advantage of any food source they come across. They will also eat vast quantities with each rat needing its body weight in food every three days. But rats ruin far more food than they consume through their dirty habits and wasteful gnawing practices. Indeed, rats will gnaw at inedible wood and concrete in order to wear down their constantly growing teeth.

The destructiveness of the rat is made even greater by its incredible fertility. Each female produces seven litters of up to fourteen young each year, and each infant becomes sexually mature within a matter of months. It has been suggested that under ideal conditions a single pair of rats might produce over ten million descendants within three years.

The disease spreading activities of the rat are every bit as destructive as their food destroying habits. The fleas which rats carry with them will also feed on humans and so spread disease between the two species. Perhaps the most notorious outbreak of rat-born disease was the Black Death of the 1340s which swept across Europe devastating human populations. The exact death toll has never been properly assessed but amounted to nearly 50% in some areas, with the plague returning at intervals over the following decades.

The rat which has caused so much misery and suffering originated in eastern Asia but is now distributed world wide. It is around a foot (28 centimetres) in length and weighs upwards of a pound (500 grams). The two main species of rat are the brown and the black, of which the brown is the larger. Both are serious pests, though the black rat seems to prefer dry attics while the brown rat prefers damp cellars and sewers. Despite the dreadful depredations of the rat the Victorians considered them not without their uses. One authority, speaking of the rats in London sewers stated that they 'perform the offices of scavengers by devouring the mass of vegetable and animal offal which is daily cast into those passages and

which would speedily breed a pestilence were it not removed by the ready teeth of the rats'.

The closely related mice can also cause damage to humans. The house mouse, for example, thrives in the warmth of houses and can spread disease and infection though its habit of spoiling more food than it consumes. Many of the familiar rustic features of agricultural buildings were efforts to combat the mouse menace. The stone toadstools on which grain stores were stood, for instance, were designed so that mice and rats attracted by the food store could not climb up to gain entrance.

Confined to Europe, the attractive harvest mouse is a major pest of grain fields. The natural home of the species is among the reeds and rushes of waterside habitats. It is an agile climber, clambering though the miniature forests of stems with the aid of its prehensile tail. It fed on the grass seeds and built tiny round nests of woven grass in which to raise its young. Such a lifestyle was readily transferred to fields of standing grain which so resembled the tightly packed stems of river banks. It light weight makes it able to clamber up wheat stems to gnaw at the ripening grains. During winter, when the grain is harvested, the mice move to hayricks where they spend cold months in warmth and security.

A specialised family of rodents are jerboas, found in arid areas of Asia and Africa. These creatures are adapted to jumping with their elongated and powerful hind limbs. The foot is as long as the shin, itself longer than the thigh. The front legs have become adapted into feeding instruments which can be used almost as hands to bring tiny pieces of food up to the gnawing teeth. The three-toed jerboa is a native of Central Asia where it survives on the open steppes by excavating long burrows in which it spends the day, emerging at night to feed. The desert jerboa of North Africa is probably the most common of the group, bounding through the sands of the Saharan fringes in search of food.

Left: Wood mice, possibly the most common mouse in Europe these creatures are rarely seen for they are shy and retiring woodland inhabitants. Bottom left: House mice, a species accustomed to living close to humans and to feeding on stored foods.

1: House Mouse.
2: Yellow-necked Mouse.
3: Harvest Mouse.
4: Wood Mouse.
5: Rock Mouse.
6: Striped Field Mouse.
7: Cretan Spiny Mouse.
8: Desert Jerboa.
9: Black Rat.
10: Brown Rat.
11: African Pygmy Mouse.
12: Three-toed Jerboa.

DOGS
Hunting with Numbers

Dogs are among the most successful predators on earth, and their place is assured by their co-operative hunting habits. Most species do not hunt alone, but depend upon co-ordinated hunting patterns to achieve kills.

The most organised of all hunters is perhaps the wolf, once common throughout Europe, Asia and North America. As large as a big domestic dog, the wolf is a powerful animal and is equipped with strong, sharp teeth and muscular jaws with which it brings down its prey.

The basic social pattern for the wolf is the pack, which consists of animals which are nearly always related to each other. Within the pack there are strong hierarchical divisions with the senior animal leading the pack in attack and claiming the choicest flesh of a kill. The size of a pack varies considerably from that of a single pair and offspring to massive groups, the size of which are still in dispute.

When hunting in pairs or small numbers, wolves tend to stick to a pattern of ruse and deception. While one wolf demonstrates in full view of the quarry, the others sneak up from a different direction to launch a surprise attack. When hunting in larger numbers stealth is often replaced by tenacity as a hunting method. Large packs give chase to quarry with the low, loping run which can cover long distances without appearing to tire the wolf. Sections of the pack will swing out on either side to stop the prey turning aside. Most large prey, such as deer and wild horses, are caught this way, few escaping once the wolf has got on their track.

In recent years the numbers of wolves have been severely reduced by man, but in the past wolves dominated the northern forests. During times of food shortage they were known to attack humans and even to gather in huge packs several hundred strong. In 1840 a traveller on a horse-drawn sledge was chased by a pack through the forest, seven of the wolves following the sledge into a barn where they were fought off by waiting grooms.

More disturbing was the way Russian wolves followed the retreating army of Napoleon in 1812, keeping pace with the column from Moscow to Germany. One terrified survivor told how he had seen a band of exhausted French infantry fighting back to back against a pack of wolves until they had all been devoured. For more than a decade the inhabitants of Germany struggled to contain the huge influx of wolves their area had suffered.

Perhaps the most familiar wild dog to Europeans is the fox which slinks through the dusk in search of its prey. Hunting various small creatures, the fox will feed on earthworms or insects as well as birds and rodents. It is notoriously cunning and will find its way through the most stringent defences to get at chickens and other domestic animals. In agricultural areas the fox is considered a major pest and is hunted ruthlessly. In recent years the fox has moved into suburban and urban areas, often moving along railway lines. Here it feeds on refuse and food scraps left by humans.

The closely related fennec fox of North Africa is instantly identifiable by its large ears. It hunts jerboas, birds and lizards in the arid edges of the Sahara where its large ears help it to locate prey in the dark.

The multi-coloured African hunting dog is widespread through sub-Saharan Africa though it tends to avoid the dense forests. The long legs of this species are a clue to its nomadic lifestyle with the packs ranging widely across the open plains in search of food. Most packs set up a temporary home base when young are born and several adults stay constantly with the cubs to guard them against attack. The other adults bring meat back to the adults and cubs after the hunt. Like wolves, the African hunting dogs rely chiefly on wearing down their prey when acting together. They are quite capable of out running large antelope and zebra and of bringing them down.

Sharing its range with the African hunting dog is the black backed jackal, which at first sight more resembles a fox. The jackal has been known to hunt in packs, but

generally prefers to hunt alone, entering villages in search of poultry or food scraps. It is hunted both to destroy it as a pest and for its valuable fur.

The wild dog of Australia is the dingo, though it is not a truly wild species. Most authorities now agree that the dingo is descended from domesticated dogs brought to Australia by the Aborigines several thousand years ago. The true-bred dingo is now a rare animal for new strains of domestic dog brought from Europe have interbred and affected the resident population. The true dingo is rather larger than a wolf, but lighter in build. It lives in family groups, but will co-operate in larger packs when after bigger quarry. Since the introduction of domestic stock animals, such as sheep and cattle, the dingo has shown itself to be an enemy of the farmer and is hunted in many areas.

Below: A pair of fox cubs. Up to four cubs are born in the spring and both parents collect food for the growing brood. Bottom: A lone wolf in Spain. Wolves have been exterminated from most of Western Europe, but small packs remain in remote regions of Spain and Italy.

1: Wolf.
2: Black-backed Jackal.
3: Bat-eared Fox.
4: Coyote.
5: African Hunting Dog.
6: Maned Fox.
7: Dingo.
8: Fennec Fox.
9: Red Fox.

BEARS
Lumbering Carnivores

Bears have come to fill an important role in human thought and folklore. Young children cuddle teddy bears or listen to the tale of Goldilocks and the three bears. Even adults use bear imagery be it to describe a bear hug or to caricature the Russian state. The roles which bears have been pushed into by human imagination are many and varied, including both friendly and vicious aspects.

Whatever their place in folklore, the bears are a formidable group of creatures. They are the largest of the carnivores, and easily the most powerful. Conversely they consume far less meat in their diet than do the other carnivores. Rather than rely exclusively on meat, the bears take large quantities of fruit, berries, insects and even grass.

The species which is most familiar, both in folklore and in reality and which is also the most widespread is the brown bear. Before the advent of man the brown bear was at home throughout the temperate forests of the northern hemisphere in both Old and New Worlds. With such a vast range it is scarcely surprising that many local races and sub-species emerged. Some of these were formerly counted as distinct species, but are now grouped together with other brown bears.

With the rise of settled human populations, bears became a major threat to livestock and humans. They were hunted relentlessly and by the close of the middle ages had been exterminated from most of Europe. So rare had bears become by the turn of the century, that they were an unusual sight. Bears captured in the Pyrenees and the Balkans were trained as performers and taken around fairs, but in Russia bear hunting became a major sport. Peasants knew that noblemen paid well for a rewarding hunt and developed a complex organisation to cater for the demand. When a large bear was discovered, the peasants endeavoured to confine it to a small area of forest and then sent a telegram to St Petersburg, now Leningrad, for circulation at court. The young noblemen then leapt aboard trains to travel to the location of the bear. The peasants made a quick profit from housing and feeding the nobility and their staff, as well as a tidy sum for reporting the bear in the first place.

The large New World sub-species known as the grizzly has suffered similar persecution and has been eradicated from almost its entire range. Only a few mountainous western regions and northern forests still hide populations. In South America the niche of the brown bear is taken by the rather similar spectacled bear which takes its name from two whitish rings around its eyes.

Unlike the brown bear, the black bear has two distinct species, the American and the Asiatic. The American black bear reaches around 6 feet (2 metres) in length and may be any shade from dirty white to jet black. It too has been driven from much of its range, but remains very common in more remote areas. Rather more of an opportunist than the brown bear, the American black bear has learnt that food scraps may be scavenged from garbage tips and that certain crops make good meals. It has therefore become something of a nuisance in many areas while its familiarity with humans can make it become classed as a danger.

The Asiatic black bear, found from the Hindu Kush to Korea, has a similar habit of raiding crops but will also attack domestic animals, including sheep, goats and cattle. It can be distinguished from its American counterpart by a white V-shaped mark on the chest.

A somewhat similar whitish crescent is found on the Malayan sun bear. Reaching only around 3 feet (1.2 metres) in length this is the smallest of the bears and is almost totally nocturnal. It feeds on birds and small mammals as well as on fruits and insects.

Two unusual bears are the sloth bear and polar bear. The sloth bear is a native of India and has become specialised for ant eating. It has a long snout and muscular lips with which it sucks up ants and larvae having first ripped open the nest with its claws. The creature is, however, capable of hunting larger game, as shown by the experiences of a British official named Watts-Jones in the late 19th century.

Watts-Jones was approaching a cave when a sloth bear emerged. 'It charged,' he wrote later. 'I shot, but failed to stop it. In his rush the bear knocked me over backward - in fact knocked me three or four feet away. When next I remember anything, the bear's weight was on me and he was biting my leg. He bit two or three times. I felt the flesh crush, but I felt no pain at all. I felt no particular terror, though I wondered when he would kill me, and thought what a fool I was to get killed by a stupid beast like a bear.' Fortunately Watts-Jones' native servants were able to drive the bear away.

Equally liable to attack humans is the polar bear, or nennook. The most famous person to be assaulted by a polar bear was the great British admiral Nelson when he was a boy. More commonly the polar bear preys upon seals and fish which it stalks through the ice floes of its Arctic home.

1: Asiatic Black Bear.
2: Brown Bear.
3: American Black Bear.
4: Polar Bear.
5: Malayan Sun Bear.
6: Sloth Bear.
7: Spectacled Bear.

Far left: A female grizzly bear with two well-grown cubs. There are several types of grizzly, but most are rare and some seriously endangered. Left: A polar bear in its natural habitat of the northern snowlands around the Arctic Ocean.

RACOONS AND PANDAS
Symbol of Survival

The giant panda has become a very apt symbol of the World Wildlife Fund, for it is not only attractive but also in danger of extinction. It also symbolises the need to discover more about the wildlife which is in need of conservation, for remarkably little is known about this animal. Indeed until a century ago science was not even aware of its existence.

It was a French missionary who, following up local tales, revealed the existence of this charming creature. Even today, a hundred years later, not much more is known about it than was revealed by the stories of locals told to the missionary.

Although it resembles a bear both in size and with its heavy body and short tail, the giant panda belongs to an entirely different group of carnivores. It lives in the inaccessible forested mountains of western China and eastern Tibet where it makes itself even more inconspicuous by frequenting the near impenetrable thickets of bamboo which abound in the area.

Bamboo makes up the vast majority of the panda's diet. It has a specially enlarged wrist bone which projects from the base of the hand to serve as a sixth finger against which the true fingers can flex to grip bamboo stems. Because bamboo is not particularly nutritious, the giant panda needs to spend some 16 hours a day eating. It will occasionally catch small birds or mammals to supplement its diet. The giant panda suffers from the fact that bamboo dies after flowering. On occasion entire forests flower at once and then die, leaving the resident pandas to starve.

Exactly how many giant pandas remain in the wild is unclear for the simple reason that it is almost impossible to count them. It is clear, however, that they are rare because of their restricted diet and the limited extent of bamboo thickets open to them. Attempts to breed giant pandas in captivity have not been successful so the survival of the species seems to depend on the fate of their numbers in the wild.

Rather more common is the lesser panda, sometimes referred to as the red panda, which is found across much of southern Asia from Burma to the Himalayas. Measuring barely 3 feet (90 centimetres) in length this creature is also a forest animal, but is more arboreal in habits. It has a more wide-ranging diet than the giant panda, taking seeds, leaves and shoots in addition to bamboo. It is also more likely to take eggs and small animals.

The raccoon family, to which pandas are sometimes linked, numbers eighteen species, all of which live in the Americas. The best known of these is undoubtedly the raccoon itself which is found in North America from southern Mexico to the forests of Canada. This heavy, squat animal is about 3 feet (90 centimetres) long and moves with a rapid, shambling gait.

Its favoured home is in forest, preferably within easy reach of water. Here it hunts for seeds, fruit, birds, mammals and even fish, all of which it consumes with equal relish. A particular delicacy are shellfish, including oysters. Raccoons prise open these tough prey by gripping the shell in their hind legs, inserting their front claws into the valve and tugging repeatedly until the shell springs open.

One of the creature's more curious habits is its food washing. Whenever it has a morsel of food and water is to hand, the raccoon will repeatedly dip the food in water and slosh it around as if washing it. It is unclear if the raccoon is actually washing its food or not. Observers have seen raccoons paddle the water even when they do not have food and to shake food vigorously in the air just as it does in water. Raccoons have also been seen to wash their young.

The omnivorous diet and inquisitive habits of the raccoon have enabled it to thrive alongside humans, invading the urban environment in recent years. When Europeans first encountered the raccoon they found its boldly marked fur irresistible as a fashion accessory. Coon hats became popular, with the ringed tail left dangling, and fashionable carriage rugs made great use of coon skins.

The coati of South American forests is in many ways similar to its northern cousin. It is about the same size and shares the boldly striped tail and muted body colour. Its diet concentrates more heavily on invertebrates, though it will take vegetable food and small vertebrates on occasion.

Though all raccoons are arboreal and nocturnal to a degree, the kinkajou and olingo take both features to extremes. The latter inhabits the lush tropical forests of Central and South America, though the latter is restricted to the forests north of Venezuela. Both species are active at night, moving through the high branches in search of fruit, insects and eggs. Indeed, the two animals are often seen together, forming mixed groups of over a dozen individuals.

1: Raccoon.
2: Coati.
3: Olingo.
4: Giant Panda.
5: Red Tree Panda.
6: Kinkajou.

Left: A juvenile raccoon. Young raccoons are born blind and do not venture outside the nest until they are about 8 weeks old, remaining with their mother for several months.

MUSTELIDS
Slinking Killers

With their short legs and long, supple bodies the mustelids are very like the earliest carnivores which hunted fellow mammals millions of years ago before the appearance of either cats or dogs. Despite this apparently primitive body pattern, the mustelids are a highly successful group of hunters with over 60 species alive today.

Mustelids are almost entirely carnivorous, preying on any small animal which they can catch. Rodents and birds make up the bulk of the diet, though large mustelids such as the wolverine have been known to bring down creatures as large as sheep. In fact the diet of individual species is determined more by their home than by their ability. The almost totally marine sea otter feeds on shellfish and sea urchins while the common otter hunts the fish, frogs and water birds of its riverside home.

There are, however, greater differences between the two species than their diet. The sea otter is large for a mustelid at over 5 feet (1.6 metres) in length and has powerful webbed hind feet which aid it in swimming. The sea otter spends almost its entire life at sea, bobbing gently in sheltered inshore waters which are rarely over 60 feet (20 metres) deep. Only during severe storms or when giving birth will the sea otter come ashore. Even then it scarcely moves beyond the reach of the spray, and dives back into the water as soon as it can.

Feeding on shellfish has presented the sea otter with the problem of cracking open the shells. Its claws are not powerful enough to prise the shells open, so the sea otter has developed the ability to use tools. When it recovers a shellfish from the seabed, it brings up a flat stone with it. The stone is balanced on the otter's chest while the prey is repeatedly hammered against it until the shell cracks.

To protect itself against the chill waters off the Alaskan coast where the sea otter lives, it has a magnificent pelt of thick, dense fur which is considered the finest of any animal. It was formerly hunted by riflemen in boats, a single pelt being worth £200 even in the 1920s. Overhunting led to the threat of extinction, but protective measures have led to an increase in numbers.

The common otter is a creature of European and Asian river banks. It excavates a long burrow in the bank, often with its entrance below water level, in which it seeks shelter. Like its marine cousin, the otter is a superb swimmer, making use of its webbed feet and strong tail when pursuing fish or water mammals.

The burrowing habit of mustelids can also be seen in the badgers, which dig sets stretching as far as 10 feet (3

Above: A European otter which is a magnificent swimmer, but has not lost its ability to run quickly on land. Left: A European badger. Bottom left: A sea otter which has wrapped itself in kelp to prevent it drifting with the ocean currents.

metres) below ground level. Badgers stay in their sets throughout the day, emerging at dusk to hunt their prey of small mammals, birds, insects and slugs. They will also take fruits when they are available. The common badger is divided into two distinct races. To the west of the River Volga the European badger is found while east of that river the sand badger thrives. The latter is easily recognised by its smaller black face stripe.

In North America the Eurasian badger's place is taken by the aptly named American badger. Like its European cousin, this creature is heavily built and feeds on a fairly mixed diet. Its facial markings are distinctive with the black cheek patch while a pale stripe runs along its back.

Rather different in habits is the honey badger, or ratel, of Africa and the Middle East. In this species the black body fur is broken by a broad pale stripe running from the head to tail. As its name suggests it has a particular liking for honey and has developed a working relationship with a small bird called the honeyguide. When the bird finds a wild bee hive, it will go in search of a ratel which it will lead, by calling and display towards the hive. The ratel readily follows, and tears open the hive, gorging itself on the honey and bee larvae within. The honey guide flutters down to join in the feast.

The ferret badger, which ranges from northern India to southern China is unusual among badgers in its tree-climbing ability. It is otherwise fairly typical, digging long burrows and emerging at night to take a wide variety of food.

1: Honey Badger.
2: European Badger.
3: American Badger.
4: Speckled Neck Otter.
5: Chinese Ferret Badger.
6: European River Otter.
7: Sea Otter.
8: Patagonian Ferret.
9: Ferret.
10: Marbled Ferret.

CIVETS AND GENETS
The Near Cats

The various species of civet, genet and related viverrids are found throughout the Old World and form a highly successful group of small hunters. In their stealthy movement and appearance they bear a superficial resemblance to cats, a likeness emphasised by their partly retractable claws and other features. For these reasons some place the viverrids close to the cats and sometimes group them together. However, the viverrids have several important distinctive features. Their bodies are elongate and their legs short, like the mustelids, and their tails much longer than in cats. But most telling of all is the dentition which in viverrids runs to 40 teeth and requires a long, pointed muzzle very different from the blunt, rounded snout of the cat.

The African civet is one of the larger species, reaching 5 feet (1.6 metres) in length with its tail. Perhaps because of its size it lacks the superb tree-climbing abilities of other civets. It spends most of its time on the ground, where it searches for its prey of reptiles and small mammals, though it will take fruit and succulent shoots on occasion. It is chiefly a nocturnal animal, spending the day in the cover of dense vegetation or skulking under logs. It is not a good digger itself but will readily take up residence in an abandoned burrow or den of another creature.

Most viverrids have pungent scent glands located under the tail with which they mark stones or trees to advertise their presence. The anal scent glands of the African civet have a strongly pronounced musk-like odour which is much in demand by the perfume industry. This fact has formed the basis for a flourishing cottage industry in many African and Asian countries for some time. The civets are kept in cages beside the house and fed with meat scraps and offal. Twice a week the animals are caught and their anal glands carefully evacuated with a small wooden spoon. The waxy secretion is then bottled and sold off to representatives of the perfume industry.

The rather smaller African palm civet, as its name suggests, is more skilled at climbing. Indeed it spends almost its entire life in the trees of its native forests which stretch from West Africa, where it is most numerous, across to Mozambique. It is rarely seen, even where it is most common, for it keeps to the densest foliage and is active only at night.

In the trees the African palm civet finds its food which features fruit and leaves more heavily than that of other viverrids. It will however take reptiles, birds and mammals whenever it can. Scampering agilly through the upper branches it will pounce on victims, clamping its jaws shut with great speed and dexterity.

The slightly heavier masked palm civet inhabits the Far East. Its range reaches down to the islands of Borneo and Sumatra, but it is more typical of northern forests on the flanks of the Himalayas and into southern China. It, too, spends most of its time in the trees, scampering in search of insects, lizards and fruit. It will come to the ground more readily than its Africa cousin, in search of rodents on which it feeds voraciously.

Perhaps because it spends more time on the ground within the reach of large predators, the masked palm civet has developed an effective chemical weapon. The anal scent glands, which other viverrids use to mark scent posts, have become enlarged and produce a noxious substance. When an intruder is spotted, the masked palm civet turns is back and sprays the scent at the predator. Most hunters are put off by the sudden onslaught of the stinking mess and beat a hasty retreat.

The coat of the masked palm civet is unusual amongst viverrids in that it is plain and devoid of the spots and stripes which make its cousins such attractive creatures. The body and tail are a uniform grey-brown, though the tail tip may have a darker hue. The face, however, is boldly marked with black and white stripes rather like those of a badger.

Very different are the genets which have poorly developed scent glands, but beautifully marked coats. Like civets, the genets prey upon a varied diet of vegetable and animal foods, but concentrate on the carnivorous features of their diet. They can generally be distinguished by the fact that their tails are longer in proportion to the bodies than are those of civets.

Genets are kept as domestic pets throughout much of their range, taking readily to human company if caught at a young age. Their chief function as pets is to keep down the number of rodent pests. One genet kept by a family in southern Italy spent its whole waking life stealthily prowling through the house and pushing into nooks and crevices in search of mice. Unlike domestic cats, genets will not play with a captured mouse, but despatch it and eat it within seconds. In the wild, genets lie up during the day in abandoned burrows or in dense foliage, emerging at dusk to prey upon whatever small creatures can be found.

1: Giant Genet.
2: Masked Palm Civet.
3: Newmans's Genet.
4: African Civet.
5: Celebes Palm Civet.

Left: A common palm civet in the Dach Game National Park of northern India. Palm civets are noticeably arboreal and take a wide variety of foods.

SMALL CATS
Silent Killers

As a group, the cats are perhaps the most perfectly formed terrestrial predators alive today. They can move with stealth and silence, creeping up on a prey animal without advertising their presence in any way. The final pounce is made with startling speed and skill, bearing down the victim in seconds and despatching it with a swift, clinical death blow. Their skill enables the cats to hunt alone, unlike dogs which rely on group hunts.

The cat which goes under more names than perhaps any other is the large tawny beast of the Americas known variously as the American lion, the mountain lion, the puma, the cougar and a host of other local names. In fact all names refer to a single species, although some localised races have been identified. It is a fairly large predator, measuring nearly 8 feet (2.5 metres) in length and being of bulky, but lithe build. Its coat is a tawny colour which lacks markings except on its face and blends gently to a paler colouring beneath.

Before European agriculture spread across the New World, the puma was to be found throughout both Americas, from the northern tundra of Canada as far south as Cape Horn. This remarkable spread took in a greater range of latitudes than the range of any other cat and embraced a similarly impressive diverse number of habitats. The puma was as much at home on the open plains as it was in mountain coniferous forests or lowland deciduous woodlands. The spread of agriculture deprived the puma of its habitats and severely reduced its numbers. When the cat turned to domestic stock as an alternative source of food, the farmers launched a programme of eradication which virtually eliminated the puma from most of the two continents. Some hunters took to eating the flesh of the puma, which they declared to be pale, firm and tasty. It is now protected in some areas and has staged something of a comeback as populations of deer and other prey have increased.

The puma hunts chiefly at night, but has been known to be active during daylight hours, particularly in more remote areas. It is a superb predator, being able to take advantage of the slightest cover in its approach to its prey, be it deer, cattle or rodent. It has been known occasionally to attack humans, particularly children, but will usually give way to determined resistance.

The much smaller leopard cat inhabits much of eastern Asia, its range stretching from the coniferous forests of Siberia to the tropical jungles of Borneo. It made its way to the Philippine islands because, unlike many cats, it is a fine swimmer and takes readily to water. Indeed the first specimen of this fierce creature ever taken alive was netted from the sea some distance from shore in the Bay of Bengal. The leopard cat spends most of the day lying beneath logs or boulders and emerges at dusk to hunt for various small animals.

Pallas's cat is a creature of the deserts, being found in the cold arid lands of Central Asia. This stocky cat has a thicker and more luxuriant coat than any other cat which helps to protect it against the bitingly cold winds of the deserts. Like the leopard cat, Pallas's cat is chiefly nocturnal emerging from rock crevices at dusk to prey on the rodents and birds of the area. Its remote home and nocturnal habits make this one of the less reported wild cats and little is known about its habits.

The open plains of sub-Saharan Africa are home to the elegant serval which can reach over 3 feet (90 centimetres) in length. Like other small cats, the serval is active chiefly at night, though it is sometimes glimpsed during daylight hours. It is a strongly territorial cat and individuals are rarely found outside their home range. Males will vigorously defend their boundaries against each other, but generally tolerate intrusions by females. It is fairly wide ranging in its diet, taking any small animals it can catch, but apparently preferring mammals to birds or reptiles.

The somewhat similar caracal shares the range of the serval but is also found in the Near East and parts of India. It has the same long legs and elegant stride of the serval and preys upon a similar variety of victims. Its coat, however, is a uniform tawny instead of being spotted and its ears bear conspicuous tufts of hair.

Ear tufts are also a feature of the lynx which ranges widely across the northern continents from Portugal through Siberia to Canada. It is thought that the long hairs serve to emphasise ear movements which indicate the mood of the cat. It hunts small rodents and similarly sized creatures, but will also tackle larger prey such as deer and wild boar. It has been known to attack sheep, killing far more than it can possibly eat, and so has become regarded as a pest in many areas.

The African black-footed cat has a beautiful coat of yellow marked with black spots and bars and ranges widely across the Kalahari and nearby plains. It is about the same size as a small domestic tabby and has been considered as close to the ancestral stock of the pet cat.

1: Caracal.
2: Puma.
3: European Lynx.
4: Serval.
5: Pallas's Cat.
6: Leopard Cat.
7: Black-footed Cat.

Left: A serval cat surveys the open plains of Tanzania's Serengeti Game Park for prey. The serval is barely as large as a domestic dog, but will tackle small antelope when hunting.

BIG CATS
The Expert Killers

The big cats are by far the most impressive and consummate hunters on earth today. Indeed, they are the only mammals to pose a regular and very real danger to humans. Leopards, jaguars and lions have all been known to prey on humans. On one famous occasion earlier this century a pair of particularly voracious maneater lions halted the building of a railway in Kenya when workmen refused to enter the territory until the lions had been shot.

The typical hunting pattern of the cat, that of lone stalking, is the most common among the big cats. The clouded leopard of southern China and South East Asia is particularly adept at dropping on to victims from trees. It will secrete itself in dense foliage above well used paths through the forest and wait for a prey animal to pass beneath. Its coat is instantly recognisable for it bears large blotches of dark coloured hair, surrounded by narrow black stripes which are very different from the tightly packed roseates of the larger leopard.

Even more beautifully marked is the snow leopard, or ounce, which inhabits the high mountain slopes of the Himalayas, Hindu Kush and the Pamirs. The coat is long and luxuriant and is marked with delicate splashes of darker roundels. During the summer the snow leopard follows its prey of ibex and wild sheep far above the tree line to the alpine meadows and snowfields of the upper slopes. When winter clamps down on the high mountains, it moves down into wooded valleys in pursuit of its victims.

The jaguar is the archetypal big cat of the New World, inhabiting the dense forests of Central and South America. It was once common on the open pampas further south where it went by the name of *tigre* and where it preyed relentlessly on the herds of cattle kept on the range. It has now been largely driven from the plains, depriving the gauchos of an alternative source of income from the skins. In the late 19th century as many as 4,000 skins were exported annually. Most animals were shot, but at least one white man, Sasha Siemel, learnt the risky Indian method of killing *el tigre* armed only with a spear. It was, he declared, better than a rifle for a spear did not need reloading.

The jaguar is a formidable animal, being only a little smaller than a lion but as lithe and nimble as a leopard. It will readily climb trees in order to drop on to prey, or will creep silently through undergrowth in order to get within springing distance of a victim. Its prey consists chiefly of sheep, deer, and the larger rodents and birds, but it will take any creature if it can catch it.

The typical hunting pattern of the cats is broken by the cheetah which inhabits the open plains of East Africa and was formerly found through the Near East to India. The homelands of the cheetah are open grasslands, devoid of cover of any kind. It is therefore almost impossible for the cheetah to stalk to within springing distance of a victim. Instead the cheetah gets as close as it can, and then gives chase at high speed.

When a hunt begins the cheetah first locates the prey with its superb eyesight, then moves cautiously toward the victim, usually a gazelle. At a distance of around 150 feet (45 metres) the cheetah breaks into a trot, then a full run. The gazelle takes fright at this point and flees. The cheetah can reach speeds approaching 70 miles per hour (115 kilometres per hour) for brief bursts and is usually able to catch up with the small gazelles. Once within reach, the cheetah will strike out with a front paw to knock the prey over before clamping its jaws around the neck.

Once the gazelle is dead, the cheetah rests for some minutes before beginning to feed. The exertion of the chase exhausts the cheetah which needs to recover its breath. Once recovered, it eats quickly, before scavengers can arrive and rob it of its kill.

The lion hunts in a similar habitat to the cheetah, where there is little cover to allow for the stealthy stalk typical of cats. Lions have solved the problem not by adapting to speed like the cheetah but by relying on co-operative hunting techniques more typical of dogs. Lions live together in highly social prides of up to three dozen individuals, within which there is a definite hierarchical order with dominant females and males. Males are occasionaly found leading solitary lives.

1: Lion (2).
2: Clouded Leopard.
3: Cheetah.
4: Snow Leopard.
5: Jaguar.

In the hunt it is the lionesses which play the major role. When zebra, wildebeest or other large victims are spotted, the pride moves out. Sometimes the lionesses spread out around the herd to take part in co-ordinated solitary attacks, but on other occasions one group of lionesses will drive prey towards an ambush laid by other members of the pride. Kills are generally shared by the whole pride, though there is a great deal of tusling and threat displays between pride members for the better parts of the animal.

Above: A magnificent male lion resting in the shade in Namibia's Etosha National Park. Males are often solitary creatures for they are driven from the pride on reaching sexual maturity.

TIGERS
Jungle Hunters

The tiger is, for many people, the archetypal big cat. It is large, powerful, graceful and extremely deadly. There is something overpowering about the tiger with its supple body and killer instinct which is profoundly disturbing and yet magnificent.

However the tiger is not a single species, there are several geographic races of tiger, which some consider to be separate species of big cat. It is generally thought that the tiger first evolved in the far north of its present range, in the chill forests of Siberia. The modern Siberian tigers are the largest of the subspecies measuring over 13 feet (4 metres) in length and being heavily built with muscular shoulders and legs. A century ago the Siberian tiger was so common that an English traveller saw three different tigers in one day, but they are now much rarer having been hunted by stockmen and fur men alike.

From Siberia, the tigers gradually spread southwards, moving to either side of the massive barrier of the Himalayas and adjoining mountains. To the west of the mountains tigers invaded the area around the Caspian Sea, where tigers are heavily furred, and now very rare, possibly extinct. These tigers later pushed over the mountains in to India where they spread out rapidly to take over new habitats and to become extremely numerous.

To the east, the tigers first established themselves in China, where a rather smaller race with a round face has developed. The tiger continued to push south through Malaysia and on to the islands of Java, Sumatra and Bali. On these islands the tigers found the supply of food to be restricted and, in common with other island species, evolved into smaller forms. The smallest of all, the Balinese reached barely 8 feet (2.6 metres) in length. The Balinese tiger is now thought to be extinct, though some unreliable reports indicate that it may survive in small numbers.

The most numerous race of all is the Indian tiger, and it is this which has been studied in greatest detail. On average Indian tigers measure about 10 feet (3.1 metres) in length and stand around 3 feet (1 metre) at the shoulder. They are powerful beasts, armed with sharp claws and powerful teeth, all of which they use when hunting.

The striking striped coat of the tiger is actually superb camouflage for it in its wandering through the jungle. The dense foliage casts shifting shadows on the forest floor, and the dark stripes cause the tiger to blend in with its surroundings. The rich orange background of its coat exactly matches the rich hues of sunset when much hunting is done.

Occasionally a white tiger will be born. These creatures are not albinos, but rare mutants in which the red coat becomes white while the dark stripes are retained. The eyes of these tigers are a disturbing ice blue. Such beasts appear in the wild from time to time and were highly prized bags in the days of hunting shikari. In 1951 the Maharajah of Rewa captured a live white tiger cub and established a breeding centre for white tigers. Many specimens of these specially bred mutants are now living in various Indian zoos.

Most tigers inhabit dense forest or open wooded country where there is plenty of cover for them to use when stalking prey. The lone tiger will patrol its territory at a steady, slow gait until it locates a potential prey. It then lowers its body and creeps silently through the undergrowth towards its intended victim. As it nears the prey, the tiger drops until its body is flat on the ground and it is advancing at a snail's pace. When close enough, usually less than 50 yards (45 metres), the tiger dashes forward, hoping to bear its victim to the ground and fasten its teeth around its throat in a deadly vice-like grip. Smaller prey are killed by snapping the neck.

Having made a kill the tiger will eat as much as it can in a single sitting. It then hides the carcass and lies up nearby to guard the meat from scavengers and returns to feast again the following night. Flesh putrifies quickly in the Indian heat, but tigers do not mind eating decaying meat and seem even to relish it.

The natural prey of tigers is varied, including as it does deer, boar, antelope and monkeys, but tends to consist mainly of the larger forest mammals. Even bison will be tackled by large and experienced tigers. Most tigers have learn to avoid humans as dangerous predators, but humans also hold tigers in respect as potential maneaters. Indeed it is as a maneater that tigers have filled their biggest place in the folklore of India.

In the old days when tigers were numerous and human populations scattered, maneating was a rare but recurrent problem. Every few years a tiger would turn maneater and prey on the terrified human villagers for some time before it died or was destroyed. It seems that such maneaters were usually old or had been injured and so had taken to the easy, but dangerous prey of humans to supplement their diet. One maneater earlier this century killed over 200 people before it was shot by a British hunter. In more recent years the growing human population has reduced the animal prey available to some tigers, while presenting them with increasing numbers of humans. As a result, fresh outbreaks of maneating occurred in the mid and late 1980s.

1: *Siberian Tiger.*
2: *Sumatran Tiger.*
3: *Caspian Tiger.*
4: *White Indian Tiger.*
5: *Indian Tiger.*

Left: A tigress stands in open country in the Dudwa National Park in India. In recent years the Indian authorities have made great efforts to set aside large areas of land for the tiger. These efforts have been rewarded with a modest increase in tiger populations.

ELEPHANTS, HYRAXES, AND AARDVARK
The Giants and the Pygmies

The largest land animals alive today are the elephants which tower over all other land mammals. The larger of the two species is the African elephant which regularly reaches 11 feet (3.5 metres) in height with one individual topping 14 feet (4.3 metres). The Indian elephant is rather smaller at an average height of around 9 feet (2.9 metres) for the bulls and slightly less for the cows.

These two species, both of which have become much less numerous in recent years, are the only survivors of a once much more numerous group of mammals. The earliest members of the elephant family lived around 45 million years ago, but it was some time before they increased in size and developed the remarkable trunk which is their chief distinguishing feature. The family diversified into a large number of different types. As recently as 50,000 years ago various species of mammoth, mastodon and elephant roamed through Europe and the Americas in addition to Africa and Asia. The collapse of elephant numbers at the close of the last ice age was sudden and catastrophic. It may have been due as much to the hunting activities of man as to the change in climatic conditions.

The species of elephants share two features in common, in addition to their massive size. Both are equipped with trunks and a pair of magnificent tusks. The trunk is an elongated nose with has become a remarkably sensitive organ of touch and scent. Its tip can be used to grip objects as delicate as a twig while the whole trunk can be used to lift trees. The main purpose of the trunk is to grasp food and place it in the mouth. Elephants feed on a wide variety of vegetation, including grasses, leaves and thin branches. A herd of elephants is capable of stripping an area of its greenery before moving on. An adult bull may consume over 400 lbs (180 kilogrammes) of fodder each day.

The tusks are enormously elongated upper incisors which project forwards from the mouth. Old elephants carry tusks of quite remarkable size. One bull shot in 1899 on the slopes of Mount Kilimanjaro carried tusks each of which weighed over 220 pounds and measured over 10 feet (3.1 metres) in length. Elephants are today usually shot before their tusks can reach such a prodigious size and weights less than half this are common. So heavy has poaching of elephants in reserves become that fears are entertained for the future of the species.

Though they are teeth, the tusks are not connected with feeding. They are used more often as a weapon. Elephants will usually attempt to frighten an intruder away by mock charges, but if this fails they will make a determined assault. One unfortunate hunter was killed by an enraged cow elephant in what is now Zimbabwe in the 1890s in an attack typical of that made by elephants. Having failed to shoot the elephant in time, the hunter was knocked to the ground by the charging beast, which then knelt down and impaled the unfortunate man on a tusk. Not content with killing its foe, the elephant then proceeded to trample his remains until it was driven off by other hunters.

The Indian elephant is more of a forest animal than its African cousin. It is also more easily trained and has long been used as a beast of burden in India. It can be trained to drag heavy loads, such as logs, or to perform delicate

Above: A herd of elephants traversing barren ground in the Etosha National Park in Namibia. Elephants need to be constantly on the move to find fresh fodder otherwise they would strip an area bare within a few days. Left: A rock hyrax in Kenya.

tasks such as unbolting and opening doors to command. Like the African elephant, the Indian elephant has suffered a fall in numbers in recent years.

The exact relationship between elephants and hyraxes is not clear. At first sight the two appear very different, but the small hyraxes have tiny hooves and are considered by many to be more closely related to elephants than to anything else. The five species of hyrax are all small creatures little larger than a squirrel which inhabit Africa and the Middle East. The rock hyrax lives in broken country and open woodland throughout Africa feeding on grasses and leaves. They are highly social animals, always being found in groups which can number upwards of fifty.

Placed very definitely in an order of its own is the aardvark which can be found in most areas of sub-Saharan Africa. The name is Afrikaans for 'earth-pig' and refers not only to its pig-like size and bristles but also to its digging talents. The aardvark preys upon ants and termites in much the same way as do pangolins and anteaters. It uses its long, powerful front claws to tear away at the rock hard termite nests until it breaks through into the interior. It then shoots its tongue out to catch any insects or larvae within reach. These are quickly swallowed and the the sticky tongue pushed deep into the nest to gather more food.

At one time the aardvark was placed together with the anteaters in a zoological group, but recent studies have shown it to have teeth and to walk on it toes, both of which features place it above its one-time relatives. It is now thought that the many similarities between the two groups are less to do with relationship than with the fact that they both lead a similar life.

1: Indian Elephant.
2: African Elephant.
3: Aardvark.
4: Rock Hyrax (5).

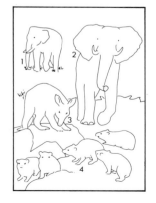

WILD HORSES
Galloping Mammals

Arguably the most elegant and graceful mammals on earth are the horses with their long legs, flowing movements and finely shaped bodies. The modern domesticated horse, with its many breeds varying from heavy shire to swift thoroughbred, is descended from the wild horses of the Eurasian steppes which were first domesticated some 5,000 years ago. Before that time horses had been just another prey animal for bands of human hunters. Once domesticated, however, the horse made life on the steppes more bearable and became a valued aid to transportation and warfare.

The wild creature most closely related to the original stock of the domestic horse is probably Przewalski's horse. This small horse is rarely over 4 feet (1.4 metres) tall and now survives only in small numbers. It runs in herds on the open grasslands of Mongolia. There can be no doubt that before the domestication of the horse that huge herds of Przewalski's horse ran wild on the grasslands, but only a few herds remain.

As with all horses, Przewalski's is superbly designed for a life on the open plains. Its head can be easily lowered to the ground to reach the grass which forms its food. The front teeth of the jaw are sharp and specialised for cropping the grass stems. The grass is then passed back to the molars and pre-molars for crushing. These teeth are large and heavily ridged and are ground continuously past each other to pulp the grass before it is swallowed.

There is no place to hide on the grasslands, so the horses have developed speed as a their principle defence against attack. Wild horses are naturally shy and will flee from danger as soon as they identify it. Few predators large enough to subdue a horse can match it for speed. Those that do attack wild horses, such as wolves and lions rely on tricks and traps to catch their prey.

Alongside the domesticated horse is the domesticated donkey which is identified by its smaller size, pale muzzle, long ears and generally more amenable temper which makes it more suitable for pack purposes. Donkeys have been domesticated for so long that it is next to impossible to be certain about their origins. However, it would seem that they were first used in the Near East, possibly in Egypt. Perhaps the African wild ass was the original progenitor of the donkey.

The wild ass inhabits the arid areas of Ethiopia and Sudan where it runs in small family herds rarely exceeding a dozen in number. Standing about 4 feet (1.2 metres) tall the wild ass can move at surprising speed, easily able to outstrip a mounted man, and travels long distances to sources of fresh water. It appears to thrive on the scanty vegetation of the desert fringes and few are found in anything but top condition. The natives of the Sudan shoot the wild ass for meat and consider its flesh to be a great delicacy. Such hunting has caused the extinction of this creature in some areas, and it is now rare across much of its range.

In Asia the wild asses are represented by a number of species of which the kiang of Tibet is the largest. Like other species of wild ass, the kiang is now much rarer than it once was. No doubt this is in part due to its curiosity. Early European travellers to Tibet were amazed to find that when kiangs spotted them they did not flee but came trotting up to the humans to investigate. More

than one sportsman found his shot at a sheep or deer blocked by a kiang come to investigate the man with a rifle. This habit has made the kiang easy to hunt, but its remote mountain home has ensured that it still survives in greater numbers than other wild asses.

The harsh mountain home of the kiang places demands on the animal which has led it to develop features not found in other animals. The most noticeable of these is the way in which the wild asses put on huge amounts of fat towards the end of summer. The thick folds of fat are laid down immediately under the skin. Here they serve as insulation during the long winters as well as providing nourishment during the months of food scarcity.

Easily the most numerous wild horses alive today are the striped zebras of Africa. There are three species of zebra, together with numerous local races. The rarest and smallest species is the mountain zebra, identifiable by cross barring on the tail root. It lives in the uplands of South Africa where it was once common, and is now restricted to a national park where it is protected. The upland range was once shared by a curious animal called the quagga, pronounced 'kwa-ha'. Striped only on the neck and shoulders, this horse became extinct about 1880.

1: Grevy's Zebra.
2: African Wild Ass.
3: Spanish Giant Ass.
4: Burchell's Zebra.
5: Przewalski's Horse.
6: Asiatic Wild Ass.
7: Mountain Zebra.
8: Chapman's Zebra.

The somewhat larger Grevy's zebra is found in northeastern Africa in the lowlands of Ethiopia and Kenya. Its stripes are distinctively narrow and form an inverted Y-shape above the hind quarters. Midway in size between the other two species is the common zebra, found on grasslands throughout East and southern Africa. The basic social pattern of these creatures is that of a dominant stallion and six or eight mares, though several such groups may gather to form much larger herds. Many localities have identifiable sub-species of common zebra. That found south of the Zambesi has faint shadow stripes between the main stripes.

Above: A Burchell's Zebra with foal in Nairobi National Park in Kenya. Zebra's give birth about once every two years and are very protective towards their young.

TAPIRS
Marsh Mammals

Tapirs are rather peculiar, pig-like animals distantly related to both the elephants and the rhinoceroses. As members of the odd-toed ungulate group of mammals, tapirs have an ancestry which stretches back to the Eocene Period, around 45 million years ago. These early tapirs were quite unlike their modern descendants, being fast moving slender creatures.

The four species of tapir alive today share a common body plan, being stocky and muscular. They appear at first sight to be similar to large pigs, with their thick bodies and strong legs. The similarity is further increased by the coat of short, tough bristles which covers the body. The image is, however, shattered by the head of the creature which carries a short prehensile trunk which is used to collect the leaves and shoots which make up its food.

Tapirs tend to frequent marshy areas in the great tropical forests which are their home. During the day they lie up in convenient hiding places, emerging at night to search for food. Passing quietly through the muddy shallows, the tapirs crop the aquatic plants which grow in profusion in the moist, hot environment. Occasionally tapirs leave their swampy homes to browse on neighbouring areas of dense foliage. In many districts this has made them a pest for a number of tapirs can do enormous damage to cocoa and other plantations.

The tapir is not a fast breeder. In the wild females produce young at a rate of about one every two years. This low rate of reproduction was suitable for a creature with few natural enemies for it prevented massive increases in tapir population above the level which could be supported by the available fodder. However, it has meant that tapir populations are slow to recover after hunting or habitat destruction by man.

The breeding process begins with a shrill and extremely loud whistle which is essential if the normally solitary creatures are to find each other in the dense forest undergrowth. Once a pair have made contact they will stay together for some weeks, feeding and sleeping together constantly. After a while, the two will gradually drift apart and eventually go their separate ways. The young is born some 400 days after conception, a surprisingly long gestation for a creature of this size.

The young is covered in stripes and spots which serve as a camouflage to protect the little creature against attack, for young tapirs are more vulnerable than their parents. The dappled coat blends in ideally with the patterned forest floor when the sun breaks through the canopy in a serious of brilliant patches.

When the tapir is aged about 7 months the light spots and stripes gradually fade to be replaced by the adult colouring. The adult Malayan tapir has a coat almost as striking as that of its young. The legs, front shoulders and head are black in colour while the flanks, back and rump are snowy white. The most likely explanation for this bold marking is that it acts as a form of dazzle camouflage. Glimpsed briefly through the forest cover, the white patch catches the eye, but since this is neither the size nor shape of a tapir it takes a few seconds for the discerner to be certain that it is a living creature which is being seen. By that time, the tapir may have moved on out of sight and so escaped the attentions of a hunter.

The three species of American tapir have a duller, brown coat which merges more gently into the background. Occasionally the dark coat fails to evade the watchful eyes of the jaguar, the greatest natural enemy of the tapir, and it falls back on a second and devastating line of defence.

The jaguar hunts by springing on to the back of its victim and attempting to bite through the neck. The tough skin of the tapir and its dense bristles mean that the jaguar takes a few seconds longer to kill a tapir than other creatures. The tapir has learnt to take advantage of this by immediately charging in to the densest patch of brush within reach. Crashing through the bushes with terrific speed, the tapir attempts to dislodge the hunter from its back, often with success.

The tough hide of the tapir, and its tasty flesh, made it a much prized prey of the local human inhabitants. The traditional method of catching a tapir was for a group of men, armed with lassoes to secrete themselves. The mating call of the tapir was then given and the men awaited the arrival of the creature. As soon as it was within range, the lassoes were thrown, and pandemonium broke out. Feeling threatened, the tapir screamed and instantly bolted for the nearest patch of undergrowth. Those who had successfully roped it were yanked off their feet and dragged after the retreating creature. Success depended on the speed with which others in the hunting band could seize the trailing rope. Hopefully the tapir was brought to a halt before it reached cover, if not the rope often broke as it was rasped against bushes and the tapir escaped. The introduction of the rifle to forest villages has made tapir hunting less demanding, but rather less exciting.

Above: A South American tapir. Early explorers of the Amazonian rainforests found that they were almost certain of a friendly reception at an Indian village if they arrived with a freshly-shot tapir.

*1: Baird's or Giant Tapir.
2: Malay Tapir.
3: Mountain Tapir.
4: South American Tapir (3).*

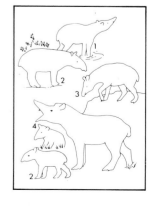

RHINOCEROSES
The Horned Charger

Considered by many old-time hunters to be the most dangerous quarry after a maneating tiger, the rhinoceros is a tremendously powerful and frighteningly unpredictable animal. One rhinoceros might gallop off at the slightest sign of a human, while another may charge with its horn lowered intent upon destroying anything in its path. Angered rhinoceroses in African game parks have overturned motor vehicles with ease, causing immense damage and some injury to those inside.

In 1837 the Englishman Captain Cornwallis Harris wandered away from his wagon and found himself confronted by a group of 20 white rhinoceroses. 'I was besieged in a bush by three at once,' he later wrote home, 'and had no little difficulty in beating off the assailants.' The no little difficulty, it later transpired, involved evading repeated charges and shooting dead four rhinoceroses which plunged into the bushes in pursuit of the unwelcome Captain Harris. Such tales were common when the African plains supported large numbers of rhinoceroses, and many travellers came home with stories of close escapes and of fatalities. One eminent Victorian traveller advised visitors to southern Africa never to hunt rhinoceros unless mounted on a fast horse and declared he would 'rather face fifty lions than one wounded rhino'.

All species of rhinoceros have now declined in number since those early days, and several are in danger of extinction. As early as the 1920s a naturalist could write of the white rhinoceros 'In 1872, whilst in Matabililand (now part of Zimbabwe) I encountered them almost daily and often saw several in one day. However, this strange and interesting animal must now be counted one of the rarest of existing mammals and in Southern Africa I fear must soon become extinct.' The creature is still classed as a rare, but is now thankfully no longer endangered.

Living on the open plains of East and southern Africa, the white rhinoceros is the largest land animal after the elephant. It stands taller than a full grown human and may be as much as 16 feet in length. It feeds on the grass of the plains, ignoring the shrubs and trees, and is found only in open areas. Unlike other rhinoceros, the white lives in family groups consisting of an adult female with young and sometimes a bull in attendance.

The species most often alleged to have a vicious character is the black rhinoceros, or keitloa, which inhabits African grasslands between the Zambesi and the Sahara. This largely due to its poor eyesight. It can scent or hear an intruder at a great distance but is extremely short-sighted and has difficulty focussing on any object more than a few feet away. It has therefore developed the

habit of charging anything which disturbs it. Sometimes the animal charges away from the intruder, but when it makes contact the result is staggering. The effect of a three ton creature striking home at full gallop, with lowered horn in action is overpowering and can sweep aside anything in its path.

Despite this a new sport among the more foolhardy Africans involves provoking a rhinoceros to charge, and waiting for the last possible moment before discharging a heavy hand gun at the creature's forehead. Such a sport is unlikely to become widely popular.

Outside Africa, the various species of rhinoceros are much rarer and are all classified as endangered. The largest Asian species is the Indian rhinoceros which stands about 6 feet at the shoulder and can weigh four tons. The most impressive feature of this creature is its thick hide which is formed into large shields of extremely tough warty skin. The folds between the thick plates are highly sensitive and are attacked by parasites. To protect itself against these insects, the Indian rhinoceros spends much time wallowing in mud, caking itself in a thick layer of impenetrable ooze which dries rock hard in the sun. Captive rhinoceroses seem to derive great pleasure from having its folds of skin scratched with sticks. The Indian rhinoceros is a solitary animal which rests during the day, emerging at dusk to browse on leaves, twigs and grass.

Considerably smaller is the Sumatran rhinoceros which is found not only on Sumatra but also through the Malayan Peninsula and into Burma. Standing only 4 feet tall and weighing only a little over a ton this creature is small for a rhinoceros and has a tiny horn barely 9 inches in length. Like the Indian rhinoceros it lives in dense forest and spends much of its time in water or mud. Exactly how many of these creatures remain in the wild is unknown, but one report placed the number at around 200.

The rarest rhinoceros of all is the Javan species of which less than one hundred survive in a reserve on Java. It is only slightly smaller than the Indian rhinoceros and also prefers dense forest with water close by. Remarkably little is known about this rare creature, which has never been common and may yet become extinct.

1: Black Rhinoceros (2).
2: Sumatran Rhinoceros.
3: Indian Rhinoceros.
4: White Rhinoceros.
5: Javan Rhinoceros.

Above: A pair of black rhinoceroses in the Ngorogoro Crater in Tanzania. Left: A lone white rhinoceros. Both species are actually grey, the chief differences being found in size and habits.

PIGS
Domestic Boars

The domestic porker which provides pork, bacon, ham, brawn and a host of other delicacies for the tables of the world is a large, heavy animal bred exclusively for its flesh. Able to consume vast amounts of food and convert them into tasty meat, the pig has become a favoured farm animal in many countries. That it will eat almost anything and requires little space for exercise has only served to increase its popularity. Generally docile, easy to handle and a prolific breeder, the pig is an almost ideal domesticated meat producer.

Its wild relatives are, however, very different kinds of animal. They are active, fast moving and belligerent. Both lions and tigers have been known to avoid tackling wild pig unless they have a distinct advantage while a British officer of the pre-war Indian army stated that wild pig 'furnishes some of the finest and most exciting sport in the world to mounted hunters armed with a sharp spear'.

The family which has produced such differing creatures is that of the suidae, the most primitive of the even-toed ungulates. More advanced even-toed ungulates include cattle and antelope, all of which chew the cud thus extracting as much nutrition as possible from grass. Pigs do not have a ruminant stomach which would enable them to chew the cud. Instead of relying on grass, they will take any food stuff which they can deal with, be it animal or vegetable.

To help them find this food they have a specialised snout unlike that of any other creature. This snout is elongated, gristly and tough, yet is extremely sensitive. Pigs can smell items of food buried some inches below ground, and root them out with their tusks. They will also snuffle through leaf litter in the hope of turning up something edible. So acute are the senses in the snout that pigs are sometimes trained to lead human collectors to truffles or other underground delicacies.

The direct ancestor of the domestic pig is generally considered to be the wild boar which formerly ranged throughout Europe and Asia. It died out in Britain during the 17th century and has since been exterminated in most heavily populated areas. In Europe populations survive in Spain, Germany and Italy, but it is more common further east.

The wild boar is rather smaller and lighter than the domestic pig, being about 4 feet long and having slender, muscular legs. Wild boars live in small groups and tend to lie up during the day and feed at night. When disturbed, the boar will fight. Charging at its opponent, the boar usually attempts to get its snout beneath the body of the assailant. A quick, powerful upward jerk of the head buries the long tusks deep in the victim and can tear it open.

Closely related to the wild boar is Africa's red river hog, or bush pig, which roams through forests and bush thickets south of the Sahara. Slightly larger than the wild boar, this pig is instantly recognisable by its reddish coat, white mane and dark face. It lives in family groups which move together through the undergrowth in search of roots, leaves, small mammals, bird hatchlings, grass, almost anything in fact. They have been known to do great damage to crops, digging up far more than they actually eat.

The warthog of sub-Saharan Africa is a similarly sized and powerful beast. It lives on the open grassy plains where it feeds upon grass and digs up various roots and bulbs. Generally considered the ugliest of the wild pigs, the warthog takes its name from the strange bumps and protuberances which adorn its face, the purpose of which are unclear. The large tusks which project up and out from the upper jaw can reach over 2 feet in length and are the principal defensive weapon of this animal. When pursued by lions or wild dogs, the warthog bolts for any shallow depression. It then suddenly swings round, sits down and presents its fearsome tusks to the pursuing hunters. So long as it can keep its vulnerable rump secure and its weapons facing the enemy, the warthog is safe.

Left: A warthog drinking at a waterhole in Etosha National Park in Namibia. Warthogs are rarely found far from water and wallowing holes.

Facial swellings are also found in the giant forest hog, where enlarged glands are responsible. Though reaching over 6 feet in length, this large animal is so secretive that science was unaware of its existence until 1904. Living in the very densest forests of central Africa it emerges at night to feast on fruits, seeds and leaves. Little is known of its habits, but it is thought that breeding pairs mate for life.

Smaller members of the pig family include the aptly named pygmy hog of northern India and Nepal. Standing barely 10 inches tall, this diminutive creature is no less aggressive than its large cousins and will attack intruders on sight. It lives in large groups known as sounders which move through the hill forests in large numbers.

The peccaries are the New World equivalent of the pigs, but the exact relationship between the two groups is unclear. The collared peccary inhabits a large range, stretching from New Mexico to the Argentinian pampas. It prefers forests, but will live in open country where it finds roots, lizards and other foods.

1: *African Forest Hog.*
2: *Wild Boar.*
3: *Warthog.*
4: *Pygmy Hog.*
5: *Collared Peccary.*
6: *Red River Hog.*

HIPPOPOTAMUS
River Horses

The hippopotamus is a strange animal which was originally found throughout Africa. On land they are ungainly animals which waddle along with their stomachs rolling about only inches above the ground. Their weight of over four tons is supported on pillar-like legs which can appear almost ridiculously short when compared to the massive bulk of the body. In size a large bull can top 5 feet at the shoulder and measure 14 feet in length.

In the water, however, the hippopotamus becomes a creature of grace and elegance. With the water supporting most of its weight, the hippopotamus is lightened and can move easily. Its legs push it forward with ease and it can swim through deep water with little difficulty. The near perfect balance of the hippopotamus' body in water is shown by the fact that when a swimming hippopotamus is shot it will exhale air and immediately sink. Within less than 3 hours, however, the incipient decomposition of the stomach contents creates enough gas to bring the hippopotamus to the surface with a rush.

It is in the water that hippopotamuses are most often encountered. They spend most of the daylight hours in rivers or lakes where they are relatively safe from predators such as lions and leopards. The hippo usually rests with only its eyes and nostrils projecting from the water surface, though in areas where it is largely undisturbed it may reveal more of itself. When startled the creature dives below the surface, staying submerged for up to 5 minutes at a time. It then reappears, looks around and if the danger is still in evidence dives again.

Though its normal defence is to dive, a hippopotamus will occasionally launch an attack at a particularly insistent aggressor. In the 1890s the naturalist F.C. Selous inadvertently became the target for such an attack. He was progressing down the Zambesi in a canoe with his equipment being carried in two other canoes paddled by locals. Rounding a corner, the party failed to notice a cow hippopotamus with her calf which immediately dived from sight. Unaware of the danger, the men pushed on until they were directly over the mother animal. Feeling threatened, the creature rushed to the surface, tipping one canoe on end. The hippopotamus then turned around and leapt on the canoe, dragging it down. The men escaped, but Selous lost most of his equipment to the muddy waters.

Though so at home in the water, the hippopotamus finds its food on dry land. It feeds on the plants which grow alongside the rivers, though herds of hippopota-

muses may wander some distance from the safety of the river in search of food on a dark night. They will graze on grass, consume foliage and pick up any fruit which falls to the ground.

Their teeth are ideally suited to such a life. The incisors are fairly long and point forwards, positioned well for digging up roots and pulling up softly rooted aquatic plants. Behind these are the canines, massive curved teeth more like tusks which sweep upwards and out. These too are used for lifting plants, but are also used in combats between rival hippopotamuses. Behind the fearsome tusks are batteries of molars tough enough to deal with the huge quantities of plants which a hippopotamus will consume.

Its lifestyle makes the hippopotamus an important creature for the rivers of Africa. By eating plants close to the banks, they keep down marsh plants which might otherwise clog the rivers and thus they keep the rivers flowing freely. The huge amounts of faeces which they deposit in the waters add greatly to the organic matter in

the waters available to microscopic life on which feed fish and other creatures.

However, though the hippopotamus is valuable to the rivers in their natural state, it is a major pest to humans living along the river banks. Not only is it something of a menace to communication, as the unfortunate Selous discovered, but it can wreak havoc on agricultural land. To a herd of hungry hippopotamuses a field of corn is little different from a stand of long grass, and is consumed with equal alacrity. It was this destructive eating which caused the ancient Egyptians to hunt the hippopotamus to extinction within a few centuries. In many other areas man has waged a similar war on the hippopotamus. The resident hippopotamus population of Natal took to eating sugar cane in huge quantities and was exterminated by farmers early this century. The shooting of hippopotamus, except in wide deep rivers, is a relatively easy affair. The hunter needs only wait for the creature to come up for breath to put a bullet in its skull.

1: Hippopotamus.
2: Pygmy Hippopotamus.

Above: A hippopotamus returning to deep water in the Okavango Swamp after spending the night feeding on neighbouring land. Above far left: A herd of hippopotamus dot the surface of the Luanqwa River in Zambia.

CAMELS AND LLAMAS
Roamers of the Deserts

Though they live in widely separated areas which had no cultural contact with each other before AD1500, the camels and llamas have been put to very similar uses by the human populations of their ranges. Both have been used as beasts of burden and their hair is collected and woven into cloth. The similarity between the uses to which the two groups of animals have been put is due to the family affinity between the two. Although the camels and llamas are very different in many ways, they share some important features.

While the pigs and hippopotamuses are even-toed ungulates which do not chew the cud, the camels and llamas have a complex, three-chambered stomach which produces cud. The system is, however, less developed than in the true ruminants and it is this which sets the camels and llamas apart. They have the ability to swallow food, part digest it and then regurgitate it for further chewing before it is swallowed and passes through the rest of the digestive system. This allows bacteria in the gut to break down the tough cellulose walls of the plant cells more efficiently and so permits the animal to gain more nutrients from a given quantity of food than other herbivores.

A second distinguishing feature of the sub-order is the structure of the foot. Only two toes are present, and the camel rests its weight on the tips of the toes rather than on the flat of the foot. Instead of ending in a hoof, as with most ungulates, the camel toes rest on broad, soft pads covered with tough plates of hard skin. When walking, the weight of the animal causes the pads to splay outwards, giving a better grip on shifting, insecure surfaces. Such a feature is ideal for the sandy deserts which are home to the camel and the treacherous mountain screes on which the llamas find their homes.

There are two species of camel, both of which have distinct geographical ranges and both of which have been domesticated. The one-humped Arabian camel originally ran free in the Arabian peninsula but is now extinct in the wild. Only the two domestic forms survive, a heavy pack animal and a lighter racing camel. It is unclear exactly when the dromedary was first domesticated, though it may have been as long as 6,000 years ago. Whenever the feat was achieved, it opened up the vast deserts to human habitation for the first time. A human on foot would soon perish in the scorching heat of the Arabian and Saharan deserts, but a camel can travel long distances. It was camel transport which enabled humans to colonize desert oases and to open up cross-desert trade routes.

As a desert creature, the camel is ideal. Its widely splayed feet are suitable for gripping shifting sand or loose gravel, but it has other specialised features as well. The danger of windblown sand is countered by extraordinary long eyelashes which keep grit out the eyes, and by nostrils which can be closed firmly at will. The lips and dentition of the dromedary have become tough and resilient to enable the creature to feed on the stringy desert plants. Perhaps most crucially, the animal has developed methods of storing both food and water. Water is stored in the first stomach while the hump is composed entirely of fat. Before starting a journey of any length, a camel driver will gauge the size of the hump and water

the camel well to enable it to survive the trip.

The slightly shorter, but sturdier Bactrian camel has its home in the Gobi Desert of Central Asia. A few small herds of wild camels still roam the open desert, but most camels are domesticated. Storing fat in two humps, the Bactrian camel lives in an even more inhospitable land than does the dromedary for while the summers of the Gobi Desert are as hot as those of Arabia, the winters are bitterly cold. The Bactrian camel has therefore developed a thick, woolly coat for the winter which is shed as spring approaches to leave the animal almost hairless.

The South American llamas are similarly present in both wild and domesticated varieties. Here, however, the domestic breeds are generally considered to be descendants of the wild forms, though they are sometimes placed in species of their own.

The commonest wild llama is the guanaco, or huanaco, which is found throughout the semi-arid uplands of the Andes. During particularly dry periods, the herds of guanaco will move down into the moister lowlands where they can find more food. Standing around 4 feet at the shoulder, the guanaco can run swiftly and nimbly across the upper mountain slopes which are its home.

The more graceful vicuna lives higher than the guanaco and frequents more lonely and remote areas. It is a highly sociable animal with bachelors moving together in herds and old males maintaining herds of around a dozen females. Its shy nature is in part explained by the fact that it has long been hunted for its magnificent coat which yields a particularly fine wool.

The commonest domestic breed is the llama itself, probably a descendant of the guanaco. Castrated males are used as beasts of burden, being able to carry loads of up to 100 pounds over the toughest mountain tracks. The bulls and females are kept in lowland pastures for breeding and their wool. Rather less common is the alpaca, a specialised domestic form which yields fine, silky wool but is of only limited use as a beast of burden.

1: *Alpaca.*
2: *Vicuna.*
3: *Llama.*
4: *Guanaco.*
5: *Bactrian Camel.*
6: *Arabian Camel.*

Below: The thick coat of the Bactrian camel which helps the creature survive the bitingly cold winds of the Gobi.

DEER
The Antlered Grazers

Deer are without doubt the most graceful mammals of the northern hemisphere. The quick, lively step of a running deer is beautiful to watch, while the timid gentle step of a grazing deer has a charm all its own. Deer are chiefly restricted to the northern continents of Europe, Asia and North America though some species have penetrated further south. They originated about 30 million years ago, possibly in North America, coming from a stock closely related to that which gave rise to giraffes and cattle.

The ruminants, a sub-order to which all deer, together with cattle, giraffes and antelopes belong, are distinguished from all other mammals by their stomachs. A ruminant has not one, but four stomachs through which the food passes before it enters the intestine. The combined action of the stomachs makes the deer and other ruminants superbly adapted for processing tough plant food into energy and nutrition, thus giving them a survival advantage over other plant eaters.

Food is cropped and hurriedly swallowed to pass into the rumen stomach. Here bacteria act on the cellulose of the plant cells to break it down. After this has happened, the food passes to the honeycomb stomach where it is shaped into small pellets. These are then regurgitated to the mouth where they are thoroughly chewed and the remaining food fibres broken up. This process of breaking up the semi-digested foods, or chewing the cud, usually takes place some hours after eating. Usually the creatures bolt down the food when in the open and exposed to attack and then retreat to more sheltered hiding places for the lengthy process of chewing the cud. This allows the creatures to spend as little time as possible in danger of attack from predators.

When the food is re-swallowed after being thoroughly chewed it passes into the manyplies stomach where it is further pummelled by muscular action. Only then does it pass into the fourth stomach where enzymes and gastric juices like those of other mammals get to work. The processed mass is then passed to the intestine for digestion.

The most primitive ruminants are the chevrotains, of which four species inhabit tropical forests in Asia and Africa. The African water chevrotain has a fine dark coat beautifully marked with stripes and spots of white. It inhabits the topical forests of West Africa where it is active at night searching for leaves, fruits and fish. It is even said that this species preys upon small mammals, being an oddly omnivorous creature for a group specialised for an herbivorous diet. The Malayan chevrotain has an unmarked coat of brown fur.

Deer are distinguished from other ruminants by their antlers. These spectacular growths are produced each year by the males, though in some species females too sport antlers. The antlers start to sprout in the spring when small growths covered with velvety skin form on the top of the skull. These growths enlarge rapidly as the bony antlers form beneath the blood-rich velvet. By the autumn the antlers are complete and the velvet dries up and is shed. The antlers are used by the males who fight each other for possession of the females. A dominant male will have a sizable herd of females under his control. When the breeding season is over the blood vessels feeding the antlers close up and the antlers are shed. The following year new, larger and more elaborate antlers are formed.

The largest of the deer is the moose, sometimes called the elk, which can stand over 7 feet at the shoulder. This big, powerful beast leads a solitary life, except during the breeding season, as it pushes its way through the forests and marshes which are its home. It feeds on leaves and twigs as well as various aquatic plants. It is to be found through the cold northern forests of North America, Asia and eastern Europe.

The red deer lives found throughout Europe, Asia and North America, though some believe that the North American red deer belong to a separate species. It is a fairly large animal, standing over 4 feet at the shoulder and sports antlers which may be over 3 feet long. Though an essentially woodland creature, the red deer will inhabit moorland and mountains in remote areas and sometimes leaves the woods to feed on nearby crops.

The roe deer is a typically European deer, though it is also found as far into Asia as China. The antlers of this three foot tall deer are rather small and simple. They never have more than three tines and lack the forward projecting tines of other species.

Smaller still is the muntjac which inhabits forested hills in southern China. This little deer is very shy and is rarely seen during daylight hours except in the earliest glimmerings of dawn. It is more often heard than seen for during the breeding season the males utter short, barking noises in the course of their battles.

About the same size as the muntjac is the Chinese water deer. As its name suggests, this species frequents river banks and marshes where it finds the reeds and rushes on which it feeds. It is the only true deer to lack antlers. In their place the Chinese water deer grows tusk-like canines which are used by the males in their fights.

1: American Moose.
2: Red Deer.
3: Roe Deer.
4: Chinese Water Deer.
5: Muntjac.
6: Asiatic Mouse Deer.
7: Chevrotain.

Left: A moose, its growing antlers covered in velvet, in the Yellowstone National Park in the United States.

GIRAFFE AND OKAPI
The Silent Ones

Easily the tallest living creature is the giraffe, which roams in herds over a dozen strong through the open forests and savannah of sub-Saharan Africa. A large giraffe may stand 11 feet at the shoulder and possess an 8 foot long neck. Exceptionally tall bulls may top 22 feet in overall height.

This exceptional height allows the giraffe to browse on succulent shoots, fruit and leaves from the tops of trees, which are out of the reach of other animals. During the full heat of the day, giraffes take refuge in shade and are active mostly during the hours after dawn and before dusk. The long, spindly legs of the giraffe are its only defence. At top speed it can outrun a horse with ease and, given a good start, can escape any predator large enough to be a danger. When cornered the giraffe can lash out with its sharp hooves to good effect and might be able to drive off a lone lion.

The advantages the long legs and neck give the giraffe are rather counteracted by their disadvantage when the animal is drinking. The structure of its neck does not allow the giraffe to lower its head to ground level without splaying out its forelegs to lower the whole body. In this ungainly position the giraffe will drink. When startled it takes the giraffe some seconds to stand erect and gallop away. Many a giraffe has fallen victim to lions while drinking.

The coat of the giraffe is exceptionally thick and tough. In old bulls the hide may be over an inch thick in places. When pursued a giraffe may well dash through a belt of thorn trees to which it is invulnerable but which will cause numerous small wounds to a hunter. The tough hide is highly prized by locals for the production of whips and other items. In the past giraffe hide shields were particularly highly esteemed.

It is the coat which distinguishes the various races of giraffe from each other. Though all giraffe belong to the same species there are numerous local races with coat patterns noticeably different from each other. Some have large brown patches with thin intervening lines, while others have broader poorly defined lines. Some have patches far more irregularly shaped than others. The geographic distribution seems to be the dominating factor in race colouration, but other factors may be at work.

The closely related okapi is noteworthy not only for its secretive lifestyle and place in evolutionary history, but also for the manner in which it was discovered. Despite its size, it stands nearly 5 feet at the shoulder, it remained entirely unknown to science until the year 1901 when Sir Harry Johnstone brought it to the notice of European experts.

In 1899 Sir Harry, a former explorer and naturalist, was made Governor of Uganda, then a British protectorate. In his earlier career as a naturalist Sir Harry had met Henry Stanley, an American explorer who travelled extensively through the unmapped Congo Basin during the 1870s and 1880s. Stanley reported the existence of two previously unknown creatures, a giant pig and a forest horse. The giant pig was later proved to exist as the giant forest hog. The forest horse was more of a mystery for the horse is a creature of the open plains. Sir Harry was intrigued, but like most other naturalists treated the reports with scepticism.

Soon after being appointed Governor of Uganda, Sir Harry released a group of Congo pigmies who had been enslaved by a German circus owner. The grateful pigmies were questioned about the forest horse and replied that they knew it well, calling it okapi. Sir Harry was delighted and, taking leave, left for the Congo with his pigmies. The Congo was at this time ruled by Belgium and Sir Harry contacted the local Belgian outpost to explain his presence.

For some days Sir Harry was led through the forest by the pigmies. Finally he had the tracks of the okapi pointed out to him. They were cloven, like those of a deer rather than a horse. No okapi could be found before his leave was up so Sir Harry retreated to Uganda with only some belts made from Okapi hide to show for his efforts. He sent these to Europe where experts pronounced them to belong to a horse, despite the tracks Sir Harry had seen.

A few months later one of the Belgian officers Sir Harry had contacted sent him a complete skin and two skulls saying that the locals had brought them out of the forest. Sir Harry sent this new evidence to Britain where the creature was at once recognised as a relative of the giraffe and named *Ocapia johstoni* in honour of Sir Harry.

The okapi itself managed to escape detection for so long because it makes its home in the densest recesses of the forest and is likely to flee at the least disturbance. It feeds on leaves and fruits which it plucks from the dense foliage. In terms of evolution, the okapi seems almost identical with prehistoric ancestors of the giraffe. It shares the sloping back of its larger cousin and has a slightly elongated neck, though this is nothing like the exaggerated structure of the giraffe neck.

1: Marsh Giraffe.
2: Baringo Giraffe.
3: Transvaal Giraffe (2).
4: Reticulated Giraffe.
5: Nubian Giraffe.
6: Okapi (2).

Left: A juvenile Masai giraffe suckling from its mother in Kenya's Masai Mara Game Reserve. The various types of giraffe are largely regionally based and are not recognised as valid sub-species by some zoologists.

OXEN
Beasts of Burden

Domestic cattle have been described as the most useful of all the domesticated animals, and with good reason. They have been put to a wide variety of purposes and have shown themselves to be ideal for most. They produce milk which can be drunk or converted into butter or cheese. Their flesh can be eaten fresh or dried into jerky for long storage. As a beast of burden, the ox has long been used to pull ploughs or wagons. In most countries cattle are put to at least one of these uses.

One of the hardiest breeds of domestic cattle is the Highland or the kyloe which originated in the Highlands of Scotland, where it still thrives. This breed sports a dense coat of long hair which protects it against the biting cold which sweeps through the glens. It is also particularly able to survive on poor fodder, thriving on coarse grass, heather shoots and other food which most breeds would find unacceptable. It is raised exclusively for its beef which many consider to be the finest of any breed.

There are many other types of domestic cattle, each produced through selective breeding to give a certain set of characteristics. The celebrated Texas longhorn, so familiar through cowboy lore of the American west, came to dominance on the windswept prairies as the only breed able to survive the bitter winters, hot summers and long cattle drives. Its meat, however, was rather stringy and as soon as better methods of husbandry made it possible the shorthorns took over as the cattle of the west. Shorthorns, a general term embracing various European breeds, are generally more docile creatures and produce better beef than longhorns. In India and China the zebu, with its pronounced fatty hump, is the most common strain of cattle.

The exact ancestry of these various breeds is lost in the mists of time, although it is generally reckoned that most European breeds are descended from the aurochs. This beast stood over 6 feet at the shoulder and was liable to charge at the slightest provocation. The last wild aurochs was sighted in 1627 in Poland. Asian breeds are probably descended from the wild zebu, now also extinct.

High on the Tibetan plateau a completely different type of cattle has been domesticated. This is the yak, the domestic form of which provides milk, yarn and meat. The wild yaks have long been driven from the valleys and plateau to seek shelter among the high crags and frozen screes of the high Himalayas. Its long hair which hangs down to encase the legs as well as the body enable the yak to survive the bitter mountain winters while the great horns are sufficient defence against natural predators.

Several wild species of cattle have defied attempts at domestication. One species which came perilously close to extinction before it was saved is the American bison, sometimes called the American buffalo. Before the advent of European civilisation on the western plains, North America supported some 70 million bison. Living off the grass these animals followed a gradual north-south migration with the seasons and congregated in such huge herds that the mass of animals could stretch out of sight, turning the whole prairie black with living flesh.

Standing over 8 feet tall at the shoulder, each individual could provide much meat, hide and bone for the indigenous Indian hunters. The arrival of rifles and railways provided both a market for buffalo meat and a means of slaughtering the beast. Large scale hunting began in the 1850s and by 1883 the last large herd was exterminated. Only rapid action by a group of volunteers saved the remaining 500 animals. Today 20,000 bison live in various reserves.

The African buffalo, by contrast, has never fallen an easy prey to the hunter's rifle and remains fairly common throughout much of sub-Saharan Africa. There are many regional sub-species of which the Cape buffalo, standing some 5 feet at the shoulder, is the largest. This muscular beast is immensely powerful and has been responsible for many human deaths. Its unpredictable temper is to blame. Individuals may lie still in heavy cover as a human approaches, then suddenly become enraged and tear forwards at a full charge intent upon impaling the intruder on its horns. One hunter shot such an enraged buffalo and sent his bearers forward to cut steaks for supper. The animal was, however, only stunned. Coming to life suddenly, it killed one man and injured many others before it was shot for a second and final time.

The gaur of India is only slightly smaller but is more inclined to flee than to fight. It inhabits forests and thickets, often in the hills, moving into the densest vegetation at dawn, emerging only at dusk to feed. Its habits and numbers are therefore not very well known, but numbers seem to be on the decrease due to hunting and destruction of habitat.

1: Ox.
2: North American Bison.
3: African Buffalo.
4: Yak.
5: Gaur.
6: Highland Cattle.

*Above: A massive North American bison on its natural grassland habitat.
Left: A yak silhouetted against the towering mass of Nuptse in the Himalayas.*

SHEEP AND GOATS
The Wool Bearers

Closely related to the wild cattle are the sheep and goats which roam widely through the northern hemisphere. Like cattle, sheep and goats have permanent, continually growing horns which can reach great lengths and are formidable weapons. Like the cattle, too, they have provided domesticated forms which have been of great use to mankind.

The domestication of both sheep and goats appears to date back some 8,000 years and in the intervening period a large number of breeds has been produced. The Merino is a fine wool breed of sheep which originated in Spain but can now be found around the world. Mountain sheep are more highly rated as meat producers and are raised in many areas. Though some sheep's milk is taken by humans, goats provide more milk particularly white breeds such as the Saanen. Weight for weight goats produce more milk than cows do and goat's milk can be used to make a variety of highly flavoured cheeses.

The domestic goat belongs to the same species as the European wild goat. The domestic sheep similarly has a wild counterpart in the mouflon which once ran wild across much of Europe. Intensive hunting exterminated it from most areas many centuries ago. It has managed only a precarious survival on Sardinia and Corsica where it lives in the rocky, inhospitable central mountains.

Standing only a little over 2 feet at the shoulder, this nimble-footed animal finds its food among the rocky crags. It appears to eat any vegetation which comes its way, which may explain how it finds enough fodder among the coarse grasses and shrubs of Corsica. Feeding in the open chiefly during twilight and lying up to chew the cud during the day, mouflon are difficult to sight. When startled the sheep dash for the nearest patch of scrub in which they then hide until the danger has passed.

During the last century several small herds were established in other European countries, notably England, Germany and Austria. Some of these still exist in more remote mountain areas.

The Barbary sheep which is found in North Africa, just across the Mediterranean from Sardinia, is rather more common. It ranges right across North Africa from the Atlantic to the Nile and is the only sheep native to Africa. The old males are imposing with their large sweeping horns and flowing beard which can reach nearly to the ground in some specimens.

The sheep inhabit the mountains which fringe the desert and cultivated areas. Moving singly or in small groups, the Barbary sheep feed on the scrubby bushes and coarse grass of the area. It does not need to live near water for it gathers all it requires by licking up the heavy desert dews. For defence the creature relies on its sandy coloured coat. When threatened it freezes and becomes almost invisible except at very close quarters.

The impressive snow white coat of Dall's sheep is to be seen in the Rocky Mountains of western North America. In summer the small herds move up on to the grassy pastures revealed by the melting snow. There the herds break up as individual animals search out their own food. When the chill winds of autumn blow, the animals gather together again and move down into the valleys to seek shelter from the bitter winter. The great curving

horns of this animal are essential to the social life of the herd. Adult males recognise each other by the greater length of the horns and fight at mating time. Rushing head on at their rivals, the males meet with a resounding crack which can be heard over a long distance. Such fights are rarely fatal, though exhaustion sometimes leads to death. Many consider Dall's sheep to be merely a subspecies of the bighorn sheep which for some reason has acquired a white coat.

Similarly clad in white is the Rocky Mountain goat which shares much of its range with Dall's sheep. These creatures live high in the most remote mountain areas and are not often seen. They live above the treeline year-round, braving the winter blizzards which drive the bighorn sheep into the valleys.

Below: A Rocky Mountain Goat and its kid. The young are able to follow the mother within minutes of birth and at only a few days old are tackling precipices human climbers might hesitate to scale.

The key to its survival in such an inhospitable home is to be found in a combination of coat and hoof. The winter weather is kept out by a rich coat which is formed in two layers. The outer coat is made up of long, coarse hair which forms an effective barrier against snow and sleet. Beneath this coat is a soft, woolly fur which insulates the creature well and keeps it warm in even the bitterest weather. The hooves of the Rocky Mountain goat are soft and spongy, but surrounded by a hard rim, a combination which gives a secure grip on loose stones and snow alike.

The chamois of European mountains is similarly limited to the highest crags. Like the Rocky Mountain sheep it has a double-layered coat and spongy hooves. It is proverbially agile and can scamper up precipices which would take a human many hours of endeavour to scale.

More visually impressive is the markhor, the wild goat of the Himalayas. An old male may stand nearly 4 feet in height, while its impressive spiral horns can reach 5 feet in length. The herds in the Hindu Kush and Afghan mountains have recently vanished from the sight of the outside world in the guerilla campaigns of that country.

1: *Mouflon Sheep.*
2: *Barbary Sheep.*
3: *Rocky Mountain Goat.*
4: *Markhor Goat.*
5: *Chamois Goat.*
6: *Dall Sheep.*

ANTELOPES
Elegant Plains Dwellers

The antelopes are a large and highly diverse group of ruminants. They live in a wide diversity of habitats and find their food in a wide variety of ways. Antelopes vary in body shape and abilit. They include such contrasting creatures as the greater kudu, standing 5 feet at the shoulder and the diminutive royal antelope which is about the same size as a hare. Such diversity is explained by the fact that the antelopes are not a rigidly defined scientific grouping, but are simply grouped under a generic name for any horned ruminant which cannot obviously be identified as cattle, sheep or goat.

The exact relationship between the various types of antelope has been a matter of hot debate, and is still largely undecided. All that can be said with certainty is that antelopes share a number of characteristics, many of which are also found in cattle, sheep and goats. Each foot ends in a cloven hoof in which only two toes reach the ground. The stomach is four chambered and utilises bacterial action to break down the tough grass on which its owner feeds. All species have permanent horns, usually present in both male and female, with which they can protect themselves against attack.

The most impressive of all antelope is almost certainly the greater kudu. In addition to its size, the kudu grows perhaps the most magnificent horns of any antelope. The female has only small horns, but the male possesses horns spiralling upwards more than four feet from the skull. When attacked by lion the kudu does not use its horns as weapons, but lays them flat along its back and flees. In this position the horns make it almost impossible for a lion to clamp its jaws over the kudu's neck.

This large beast once ranged across all of eastern Africa

from Ethiopia to the Zambesi. However the combined depredations of trophy hunters and of a disease known as rinderpest devastated the populations and greater kudu are now restricted to various isolated patches of land. They live in areas of thick undergrowth, feeding off the leaves and shoots of bushes rather than the intervening grass favoured by most antelope.

The impala of East Africa has a defence against attack every bit as unusual as that of the greater kudu. It frequents more open ground than the greater kudu, feeding on grass rather than on leaves and shoots, and relies on speed to escape its enemies. When startled the impala runs off at high speed, but suddenly interrupts its flight to leap high into the air. On landing, the antelope continues running. These antics might be a device to confuse predators. A lion closely following an impala could well be thrown off its stride when its quarry suddenly shoots upward.

One of the smallest and most delicate antelopes is the oribi which is found across the open plains of East Africa, though it prefers to stay near water. The dainty little animals move elegantly on their hooves in a gait which has been described as mincing. Each family of oribis has is own territory which is marked by scent and from which the individuals rarely stray. They emerge at dusk to graze and feed on leaves and shoots, disappearing into cover soon after dawn. Only the male possesses horns, which are rather short and straight. The females lack horns and when danger threatens they will crouch, hoping to blend in with the long grass or shrubs in which they find themselves. The closely related steinbok leads a similar life.

Much larger is the nyala which has curious barred markings on its back and flanks. This creature has a very restricted range, never being found outside the southeastern corner of Africa. Travellers in the last century reported that the nyala was highly numerous within its range and was often encountered in herds of up to two dozen individuals. During the 1890s, however, rinderpest devastated the nyala population and firearms were introduced to the area. Together the two events altered the actions of the nyala. It became rare to encounter groupings of more than half a dozen, and the creature was rarely seen at all. During daylight hours it kept to dense scrub and forest, emerging to graze only as sunset cast twilight over the plains. In recent years the numbers have picked up again, and sizable herds are again being encountered.

Adopted as the national symbol of South Africa, the springbok is one of the most numerous of all the antelope. When Europeans first pushed into the interior of southern Africa they were amazed at what became known as the trekbokken, the journey of the antelopes. In the dry season immense herds of springbok would gather together before setting off in search of damper areas with better fodder. Some years more than a million animals would join the trekbokken. When cattle and sheep were introduced the trekbokken became a great worry for it stripped whole ranges of grass and led to starvation of livestock. Thousands of springbok were shot, but they still remain numerous throughout their former range.

1: Springbok.
2: Impala (3).
3: Kudu (2).
4: Oribi.
5: Steenbok.
6: Nyala (2).

Left: A mother springbok with its new-born calf. The springbok was named by early Boer settlers impressed by the antelopes leaping abilities.

Though antelopes all conform to a basic pattern, having horns, cloven hooves and four-chambered stomachs among other shared features, there are some quite remarkable variations from the standard antelope of popular imagination.

Perhaps none is so ungainly as the gnu or wildebeest which, with its odd, stiff-legged gait, is so different from the graceful antelopes which race across the plains. There are two species, of which the larger and more numerous is the brindled gnu. Spread from the Vaal to the northern slopes of Kilimanjaro, the brindled gnu is a familiar beast on the open plains and features in many wildlife films. It gathers in sizable herds to feed upon the lush grass of the plains and drink from the many rivers and water holes. It consumes more water than most antelope and so is rarely found far from rivers.

The rather smaller white-tailed gnu existed in large numbers south of the Vaal to the Orange river, but the spread of agriculture and the activities of hunters severely cut its numbers. By 1899 only 500 existed, protected by local farmers. When the Boer War broke out it was confidently predicted by naturalists that the white-tailed gnu would be one of the first casualties. In fact the species survived and today thrives in reserves.

Almost equally awkward in appearance and movement is the haartebeest which ranges widely across the grasslands of sub-Saharan Africa. There are several types of haartebeest which go by a wide variety of local names, but all have several features in common. When seen in profile they have backs which slope down from the shoulders to the rump quite noticeably. The head is topped by a strange bony growth from which spring the horns. These first grow outwards before turning back in and, in some species, twist back out again. This odd path gives the outline of a lyre. Haartebeest inhabit open plains and are often found mixing freely with zebra.

Further removed in form from the standard antelope body plan is the gerenuk of East Africa. This lithe, slender animal frequents the edges of thorn forests and thickets. The immediately noticeable feature of this creature is its elongated neck on top of which is perched a small head which bears horns only in the male. As with the giraffe the long neck is an aid in feeding. The gerenuk browses on the leaves of the thorn and acacia, nibbling them delicately from between thorns with it mobile lips. To reach higher branches the gerenuk will not only use its neck, but also rears up on its hind legs, using its front legs to balance itself.

The diminutive grey duiker which stands barely 2 feet tall is more antelope-like in shape but its size marks it out as an oddity. It inhabits what in southern Africa is termed bush country, that is grassland interspersed with patches of scrub and trees. It may also be found on open grassland or in open woodlands where it feeds on almost anything which comes its way, be it grass, fruit or insects. This small creature is exceptionally common throughout its sub-Saharan range and there are few, if any restrictions on its hunting. Locals can add a useful supplement to their income by taking duikers and selling the skins.

Like the white-tailed gnu, the bontebok was nearly exterminated during the Boer War. By the outbreak of that conflict there were less than 300 bontebok surviving in their home range of western Cape Colony. These were preserved by local Boer farmers on cattle land where they were fenced in and tolerated alongside domestic stock. Since that low point, the bontebok has bred prolifically and several herds have returned to the wild. This graceful animal is now running free again after a gap of nearly a century.

The striking sable antelope inhabits the open grasslands of East Africa from the Vaal north to the Kenyan border. Its body is typical of several of the larger antelope, but its horns are unique. Elegantly curved, these horns reach over 5 feet in length and are formidable weapons. One coffee farmer went after a small herd of

Far left: A herd of gnu at a waterhole in Namibia.
Below: The herbivores of the African plains can co-exist as each exploits a different source of food. Here are seen a gemsbok, a zebra and a giraffe.

sable antelope with a pack of 10 dogs. While the cows fled, the large bull antelope turned to hold off the attackers. Dodging attacks nimbly and darting forward with his horns whenever possible, the antelope killed four dogs and wounded four more before the farmer called his pack off.

The most elegant of all the antelope are without doubt the various species of oryx which inhabit arid areas of northern Africa and Arabia. These graceful creatures possess magnificent horns and are beautifully marked. It is thought that oryx never drink, taking in enough water through the moisture in the desert plants which they eat. Happy in temperatures of up to 120° Fahrenheit, oryx are the largest mammals to take to a life in desert environments. They are now rare, and one species survives only in captivity.

The pronghorn is very antelope-like in appearance, but in fact belongs to an entirely different group of ruminants. The pronghorns evolved in North America and once dominated the plains. They were, however, displaced within the past 2 million years by deer and bison. Only the one species survives today, a fairly small creature with a surprisingly good turn of speed.

1: Brindled Gnu (3).
2: Topi.
3: Bontebok.
4: White Oryx.
5: Gerenuk.
6: Sable.
7: Gemsbok.
8: Pronghorn.
9: Grey Duiker.

RATITES
Giant Birds

Birds have feathers. This is the single most distinctive distinguishing mark of the entire class for all birds have feathers and no other type of animal can boast them.

The very first bird lived around 160 million years ago, at a time when the largest dinosaurs of all stalked the earth. This creature has been named *Archaeopteryx* by scientists and, although undoubtedly a bird, it has some very unbird-like features. In addition to claws on the front limbs it has reptilian teeth and a long bony tail. This fossil shows that birds evolved from reptiles, but leaves open the question as to which group gave rise to the avians. Some scientists feel that animals related to crocodiles are the best candidates while others argue that it was dinosaurs which became birds.

All are agreed, however, that a key feature in the rapid success of the birds was their ability to fly using feathered wings. With this power they could outfly the winged reptiles known as pterosaurs and establish their complete dominance of the air. Flying mammals in the shape of bats have been largely confined to specialised night-flying and winged reptiles were driven to extinction many millions of year ago.

It is all the more surprising, therefore, to find that several birds have lost the ability to fly to adopt of a completely earthbound existence. These birds, known collectively as ratites, are not particularly closely related. They are quite separate types of bird which have acquired their flightless condition for similar reasons.

The largest of the ratites, indeed the biggest bird of all, is the ostrich of the grasslands of sub-Saharan Africa. A large cock bird can top 8 feet in height and may weigh anything up to 350 pounds. It is scarcely surprising that with such a great weight the ostrich cannot fly, it has become adapted to running instead. Its legs are long and powerful, capable of powering the bird at around 25 miles per hour.

This turn of speed has made hunting the ostrich, a potentially rich source of food, a problem for tribesmen. The Bushmen developed the trick of removing ostrich eggs from the nest and crouching in their place. When the parent bird arrived, the Bushman would leap up and spear it before it recovered from its surprise. Less imaginative tribes relied on lassoes thrown from hiding. The Arabs of North Africa developed the technique of shooting the birds while riding beside them at full gallop. The feat was described as being both extremely difficult and highly thrilling. During the 19th century male ostrich plumes became valuable as fashion accessories and ostrich farms were set up, not only in Africa but also in America. Today ostriches still roam across much of their original home, though they may be extinct in Arabia and neighbouring sections of North Africa.

The rhea of South America has experienced a similar reduction in range this century. They formerly roamed across all the open grasslands of South America, but are now largely restricted to the Andean foothills. The two species are similar both in size and habits. Standing about 5 feet tall, rheas are exceptionally fast runners, being able to outdistance a horse with ease. They feed on seeds and insects which are found in abundance on the grasslands. Each cock bird maintains a harem of four or five hens, all of which lay their eggs in a communal nest where they are incubated by the cock.

The other large ratite of open grasslands is the emu, which inhabits the central plains of Australia. Unlike the ostrich and rheas, the emu is still to be found across most of its original range. This is rather surprising for it has been persecuted by man more than any other ratite. Its liking for eating crops and the tastiness of its flesh has led to recurrent onslaughts by human hunters. One attempt by a state government to eradicate emus from an important farming area involved hundreds of troops armed with machine guns. Within a few months of the emu slaughter the birds were back in as large numbers as ever.

Inhabiting the dense forests of northern Australia and adjacent islands the various species of cassowary have formed into at least 30 subspecies and localised races. Many of these races are native to particular islands, the long isolation of breeding populations being responsible for the number of slightly divergent features. The birds live singly, pushing their way through the dense foliage in search of the fruits and shoots on which they thrive. When startled the birds lower their heads and dash through the foliage at apparently suicidal speeds. The heavy bony crest on their heads protects them from fatal injuries which might be sustained by running into branches.

The island nation of New Zealand is home to the kiwi, one of several flightless birds on the islands. With no native mammalian predators to make flight necessary the birds of New Zealand have shown a tendency to become earthbound. The kiwi is the smallest ratite, being smaller than the average turkey. They inhabit the dense forests and undergrowth of the islands, snuffling their way along in search of the worms and other invertebrates on which they live. They have suffered somewhat from introduced predators, such as dogs, but their status as national symbol seems to ensure that they will be well looked after by the human inhabitants of the islands.

1: Ostrich (3).
2: Rhea.
3: Emu.
4: Bennett's Cassowary.
5: Kiwi.
6: Cassowary.

Left: A group of ostrich chicks cluster in the shade cast by an adult male in order to escape the burning heat of the Namibian sun.

PENGUINS
Swimmming Birds

With a total of eighteen species, the penguin group is one of the smaller orders of birds. It is also one of the most unusual groups for not only have the penguins lost the ability to fly, they have become adapted to an almost wholly marine lifestyle. The restricted distribution of the birds has made the discovery of fossilised ancient forms unlikely. However, it is known that the penguin group was already fully developed and widely distributed some 40 million years ago. Clearly the body plan of the penguin was evolved early and has scarcely changed since. The present day species are little different from the fossil penguins which are occasionally found.

As a group penguins are restricted to the southern hemisphere with most species breeding on Antarctica and nearby islands. The only exception being the Galapagos penguin which breeds on the islands of that name. It is only in the breeding season that the penguins come to land, spending the rest of their lives at sea.

Penguins nest together in large colonies, sometimes numbering hundreds of thousands of birds. Some species congregate near the coast, but others move far inland to find sheltered nesting grounds which have been used by generations of penguins. The Emperor penguin, the largest species of all, nests at inland sites. The birds come ashore as the autumn closes in and shuffle across the snow and ice to reach their ancestral breeding sites. Here they pair off and the female lays her egg. The single egg is scooped up by the male who balances it on his feet, encasing it in a soft fold of feathery skin. The females then return to the sea to feed, while the males gather together in vast numbers, their precious eggs protected against the cold.

For over two months the males huddle together in the bitter Antarctic winter. Then, as the eggs hatch the females return to take over care of the chick while the males take to the sea in search of food. The pair care for the chick together until it is old enough to take to the seas in search of its own food.

Other species have a similar breeding cycle in which the birds come ashore to lay their eggs and take their turns in caring for the young. When not at the breeding grounds, the birds are constantly at sea. Indeed their comical shuffling on land is due to the fact that their bodies have become adapted to swimming with only slight concessions to movement on land.

The wings of the penguins have evolved into narrow, flipper-like limbs. These are ideal for powering the bird through the liquid water in much the same way that other birds use larger wings to fly through the air. The broad feet are used as rudders to assist the bird in changing direction. With these fetures the penguins are able to dash through the water at speed, snapping up vast numbers of fish. They are also able to escape the attentions of most predators. Only killer whales and leopard seals are swift and agile enough to catch penguins. The seals have developed the habit of cruising under the shelf of floating ice floes and pouncing on any penguins which dive into the water.

To protect their bodies against the extreme cold of the frozen southern oceans, the penguins have a superb coat of feathers. These plumes are short and densely packed covering every inch of skin with a thick layer of

Above: *Emperor Penguins standing on the Antarctic ice.*
Left: *Gentoo Penguins gather on the shore of New Island before plunging into the sea in search of fish.*

insulation. The surface of the feathers is slick and waterproof keeping the inner layer of feathers dry and full of trapped air while at the same time reducing water resistance when swimming.

Each species of penguin has its own peculiarities and traits. The massive emperor penguin, standing over 4 feet tall when on the ice is the largest of all and has the longest incubation period, which in part explains its curious and unique breeding cycle. The much smaller little blue penguin is only slightly over one foot long and has an unusual blue sheen to its plumage. It is particularly common off the coasts of Australia and New Zealand where it breeds in burrows or rock crevices.

The chinstrap penguin has a similarly localised distribution being found around the South Orkneys and neighbouring islands. The numerous adelie penguin, however, is widely distributed around Antarctica and breeds in huge colonies which can cover many acres of squaking, chattering birds. Some species have yellow tufts of feathers behind their eyes, but the purpose of these flashes remains obscure.

1: *Gentoo Penguin (2).*
2: *Emperor Penguin (3).*
3: *Royal Penguin.*
4: *Adelie Penguin.*
5: *Yellow-eyed Penguin.*
6: *Magellanic Penguin.*
7: *Little Blue Penguin.*
8: *Rockhopper Penguin.*
9: *Chinstrap Penguin.*

GREBES
Diving Birds

Grebes are birds of the freshwater and are distributed throughout the world, although most species are to be found in the Americas. Composed of 18 species the group features several small birds many of which are not termed grebes but go by such names as dabchick. They are graceful swimmers and are often colourfully marked with bright plumage and various tufts or crests.

Grebes live on freshwater, diving for their food and like several other orders of aquatic bird the grebes have their legs placed well back on their bodies. This makes swimming easier for the body is pushed through the water from behind rather than dragged along from in front. This makes possible greater control and more delicate manoeuvres when under water. The grebes are famed for their acrobatic skill in the water and are able to change direction at lightning speed in pursuit of their quarry. The various species take different prey depending on their size and home range, but most concentrate on small fish, shrimps water insects, molluscs and some vegetation.

These birds are unique in that feathers form a part of their diet. The birds eat quantities of their own feathers which they are totally unable to digest. Why they should have taken to this odd habit has never been properly explained. It may be that the presence of indigestible roughage aids digestion in some way.

As a group the grebes are poor fliers having much difficulty in getting airbourne. This fact has led to the development of several localised species of grebe in isolated habitats. The Falkland Islands, for instance, have their own unique species of grebe. Presumably at some distant time some grebes arrived on the islands, found a suitable habitat, and thereafter evolved in isolation until they produced their own species.

At 20 inches in length the largest member of the group is the great crested grebe which may be enountered across most of Europe and central Asia as well as isolated populations in Africa and Australasia. It is instantly recognisable by its impressive head plumage. The white neck is topped by a crest of stiff black feathers jutting back from the head. During the breeding season this is augmented by a frill of reddish feathers around the back of the head which frames the face. In the 19th century grebe feathers were much in demand as fashion accessories and the bird was hunted ruthlessly. At one time it was feared that it might become extinct across much of its European range, but its numbers are now booming again.

Like all grebes, the great crested grebe builds a nest of twigs and decaying vegetation which floats loose on the surface of lakes and slow flowing rivers. Both parents play a role in incubation and chick care. When the chicks are still young the parents often carry them on their backs while swimming in search of food.

Very much smaller is the dabchick, occassionally referred to in literature as the little grebe. This 10 inch bird inhabits most of Europe, southern Asia and sub-Saharan Africa. The plumage of the dabchick changes with the seasons. In summer the main colour is charcoal with bright chestnut flashes on the cheeks and throat. When winter draws in the chestnut fades to a dull brown while the charcoal becomes dark brown.

The eggs are laid on a floating nest of waterweeds and twigs, but the dabchick has the odd habit of leaving its eggs alone for long periods. Either parent may incubate, but they are liable to swim off, having first draped waterweed over the eggs as a camouflage. Presumably the eggs can bear being cooled without harm to the embryo.

Inhabiting a range further north, across Eurasia and into North America is the slavonian grebe, often termed the horned grebe. Like the great crested grebe, this bird adopts a fine breeding plumage consisting of a pair of bright yellow stripes rising back across the head from the eyes to end in prominent tufts. Courtship is further enhanced by an elaborate dance in which the pair swim together and rear up out of the water to display their fronts to each other.

The black-necked grebe has a more diverse home range with breeding colonies in the Rocky Mountains, East Africa and Europe. The birds are primarily at home on lakes in open grasslands where they feed upon fish and aquatic insects, but may also be found in estuaries and beside slow moving rivers. The pied-billed grebe of the Americas and the red-necked grebe which is found in both the Old and the New Worlds are medium-sized grebes which share most of the habits of other birds of the group with their diving in search of fish and awkward walk on land.

1: *Black-necked Grebe.*
2: *Great Crested Grebe (2).*
3: *Red-necked Grebe.*
4: *Slavonian Grebe.*
5: *Pied-billed Grebe.*
6: *Little Grebe.*

Left: A Slavonian grebe on its floating nest. Far left: A red-necked grebe drifts sedately on a lake in North Dakota. All grebes build floating nests out of decaying plant matter.

TUBE-NOSED BIRDS
Long Range Fliers

The wandering albatross is familiar to many not so much for its natural features as for its alleged supernatural gifts. The folklore of the albatross is tied up with the days of sailing ships when tales told by sailors lost nothing in the retelling and every co-incidence could lead to a superstition.

The reasons why the wandering albatross became the centre of such a huge volume of folklore are not difficult to find. Sailing ships were entirely at the mercy of the weather and violent storms meant discomfort and danger to the men who sailed the seas. On long voyages the sailors were completely cut off from the rest of humanity for they had no radios. Entering the dreaded waters off Cape Horn or sailing into the 'roaring forties', such ships often fell in company with an albatross. Miles from land and often beset by storms, the ship would find itself being followed by the silent bird with its broad wings and effortless flight. The birds would seem to relish the storms which were hated by the men and might follow the ship for hours on end.

It is scarcely surprising that various superstitions should grow up around the majestic bird of the storms. The most insistent was that an albatross must never be harmed. It was this tale which the poet Samuel Taylor Coleridge picked up and used as the basis for his masterpiece *The Rhyme of the Ancient Mariner* in which a sailor shoots an albatross and is then wafted on a strange and mystical journey.

The bird which has unwittingly given rise to such tales is a truly magnificent creature. It has the greatest wingspan of any flying bird, with some individuals measuring 13 feet from wingtip to wingtip. With these long, narrow wings the wandering albatross is ideally suited to a life gliding over the windswept southern oceans. The aerofoil shape of the wings is adapted to gliding flight in high winds. The birds stay close to the water surface, rarely rising to more than 50 feet, and take advantage of changes in wind speed, disrupted air currents and overspills brought about by the wind racing over and between the mountainous waves. The birds have been seen to stay aloft for hours without flapping their wings at all. Higher winds make for easier flight for the albatross, which may explain why the sailors alleged it was the bird of storms.

The birds feed on fish and squid which they snap up from the surface by swooping down, plunging their beaks into the sea and soaring high again with their meal. Ever opportunists, the birds take any food scraps floating on the surface. It was their association of ships with discarded scraps which caused them to follow ships so assiduously.

The upbringing of such a large bird is a lengthy affair for the parents must care for their offspring until it has mastered the art of gliding flight and is large enough to cope with the strongest gales. This limits the birds to breeding once every two years when a single egg is laid. The birds appear to pair for life and nest on remote, isolated islets of the southern oceans.

About half the size of the wandering albatross, but no less graceful is the light-mantled sooty albatross. This bird soars over the same wind-lashed seas as its larger relative and preys on fish though it, too, will take scraps

cast overboard from ships.

The related petrel family includes various smaller birds with long thin wings which are distributed around the world and often undertake long migrations. The Manx shearwater is common in both the Atlantic and the Pacific and returns to the same nesting ground year after year, despite having travelled several thousand miles southward in the intervening winter. They cruise above the sea searching for fish or squid near the surface. When a victim is spotted, the bird dives down, often plunging right into the water in an effort to seize the prey in its beak.

The fulmar gained its name, originally rendered as 'foulmar' from its unpleasant habit of vomiting an evil smelling substance at intruders or when disturbed. It is a fish-eating species which has taken to following fishing boats in search of scraps and has become extremely common due to the increasing amount of food it can pick up from human fishers.

Leach's and Wilson's petrels are both fairly small, dark coloured birds which follow ships. The latter is particularly common, nesting in vast colonies of tens of thousands of breeding pairs. They cruise the skies above the North Atlantic appearing to spend the winter at sea and only coming to land during the breeding season.

1: *Light-mantled Sooty Albatross.*
2: *Wandering Albatross.*
3: *Manx Shearwater.*
4: *Leache's Petrel.*
5: *Wilson's Petrel.*
6: *Fulmar Petrel.*

Above: A wandering albatross at rest on its nest on an Antarctic island. Left: An adult wandering albatross spreads its wings beside the darker chick which is has been feeding.

PELICANS AND ALLIES
Pouched Throat Birds

The 60 or so species of aquatic bird which are included in the order Pelecaniformes are spread around the world in a wide variety of habitats and climates. All share characteristics which are brought to their greatest development in the pelicans after which the group is named.

The most distinctive feature of the group is to be found in their feet. The four toes are all of approximately equal length and are linked by a web of skin. No other group of birds has all four toes webbed together. The feature is no doubt an adaptation for swimming. The large surface area of the web skin gives a firm purchase when the foot is thrust back, powering the bird through the water with efficiency. Many species in the group rely on diving to catch their food, so powerful swimming is of great importance.

All Pelecaniformes birds have a throat pouch, known as a gular, which is used to hold fish or as a hunting aid. In some the pouch is barely visible, but the pelicans have a huge and highly conspicuous pouch which has become famous for 'holding more than its belly can'. In fact the capacity of the pouch is greater than that of the stomach, but it is rarely full of food for it is used more as a trap than a food storage organ.

The various birds in the group have fairly uniform breeding habits, though there are variations between individual species. They tend to build poor nests in large colonies, with some species laying the egg directly on to the ground. Both parents take turns incubating the eggs, of which there are rarely more than six, until the chicks hatch as blind and often naked individuals. The chicks are then fed by both parents by means of regurgitation until they are old enough to fend for themselves, at about the age of two months.

Of the six families of birds included within the Pelecaniformes the tropic birds are the least numerous with only one genus and three species. As their name suggests the tropic birds are restricted to tropical areas of the world. They are true seabirds which frequent waters in the centre of oceans which are as far from land as it is possible to get. They fly well, as might be expected of such long distance travellers, cruising above the ocean at a height of around 50 feet.

When hunting, the tropic birds fly while studying the water beneath them. When they glimpse a potential victim close to the surface, they hover to assure themselves of the possibility of a catch and then plunge down. The birds do not relish the water and take to the air again as soon as possible.

In the days of sail, mariners often referred to these birds as bosun birds, though exactly why is unclear. The high pitched scream of the bird's cry is held by some to be the reason for the name for it resembles the whistle used by bosuns to pass orders. Others maintain that the name was gained because the elongated tails of these birds closely resembled a marline spike used by that petty officer to splice ropes.

As befits their marine lifestyle, the tropic birds breed on remote oceanic islands. They make no nest at all, merely laying their egg on an isolated ledge or in a sheltered hollow. The birds fiercely protect their egg, pecking and lunging at intruders, and remain close to the egg even when physically pushed away.

The second family within the order are the pelicans themselves. These are the largest birds in the order, reaching 5 feet in length, and in them the characteristics of the group reach their extreme forms. The throat pouch is most obvious in the pelicans, largely because of the large size of the bill which may be over 2 feet in length. It is when fishing that the large beak and even larger throat pouch come into their own.

The pelican uses its beak as a type of net. Plunging its mouth into the water, the pelican gathers up some 3 gallons of water in a single gulp. This is allowed to drain out through a partially open beak, leaving any fish behind to be swallowed. Pelicans will often hunt co-operatively. Forming a large horseshoe shaped line on the lake facing the shore, the birds thrash the water with their wings as they move forward. Any fish within the arc of birds are driven towards the shallow water fringing the shore. When the fish are concentrated together densely enough, the birds plunge into the seething mass dipping their beaks repeatedly to scoop up as many fish as possible. Pelicans will also fish in smaller formations on open water, sometimes forming a tight group around a shoal of fish.

The only pelican not to fit this pattern of feeding is the brown pelican of the Caribbean and adjoining areas. As the only marine pelican its different feeding technique is probably due to the conditions of life at sea. Rather than cruise across the water surface, the brown pelican flies at a height of around 30 feet, though it may attain much higher altitudes. When a victim is spotted, the bird folds its wings and plummets from the sky in a rather fluttering, graceless manner. The large bird strikes the water with a big splash and loud impact.

1: *Brown Booby (2).*
2: *Blue-eyed Shag.*
3: *White Pelican.*
4: *Australian Pelican.*
5: *Cormorant.*
6: *Masked Booby.*
7: *Gannet.*

Left: A pair of blue-eyed shags which hunt fish by diving beneath the surface of the water.

In order to reduce the force of the blow air sacs are located beneath the skin of the breast and the neck is bent back in an S-shape to reduce the pressures exerted on the skull. This has the unfortunate effect of greatly increasing the bouyancy of the bird thus stopping it from penetrating far beneath the water surface. Within a second or two of impact, the bird returns to the surface, usually tail first as the bouyancy of its air sacs takes over from the downward momentum of the dive. Like its freshwater cousins, the brown pelican takes a huge mouthful of water and fish. As it surfaces, it raises its beak from the sea to drain the water before swallowing the fish.

The freshwater species of pelican live in dense colonies, not only during the breeding season but throughout the year. Such numbers of heavy birds make incessant demands on the fish populations of the lakes where they live. For this reason pelicans are most often found on vast lakes, particularly those of East Africa which are frequented by the white pelican. These lakes may cover many hundreds of square miles and support massive populations of fish. Some of the East African lakes contain more species of fish than any other lakes in the world and so are ideal habitats for the pelicans.

The generous amounts of food available make the lakes ideal as breeding grounds. Like others in the group, pelicans nest in great colonies of many hundreds of pairs. The nest itself is an unimpressive structure of twigs and sticks which may be built in a tree, a bush or on the ground. When the three or four young hatch out they are completely blind and naked. Indeed they are so helpless that they are barely able to move. The adults feed the young birds on a semi-liquid mush of part digested fish which they regurgitate and pass to the hatchlings' mouths. As the young grow, they become able to take pieces of food from their parents. Within two months of hatching the young pelicans are able to lead independent lives.

Known to scientists as the sulidae, the gannet family includes not only the three species of gannet but also six species of boobies which live in tropical areas. These birds are smaller and less bulky than pelicans, but are still sizable creatures being between two and three feet in length. The gannets were originally termed 'sea-geese', their present name being derived from an antiquated form of gander.

Like brown pelicans, the gannets feed by plunging into the sea from a height in pursuit of fish. They are, however, much more adept at this activity than the brown pelican. Flying in flocks of up to 100 individuals the gannets patrol the inshore waters around the rocky coasts which they favour. When the flock comes across a school of fish, the birds begin the diving routine for which they are best known.

Having spotted a victim, a gannet will push its head forward and pull its wings back to form a steep V shape. The trailing edges of the wings are used to steer the bird in its high speed plunge. As the bird approaches the water, the wings are pulled right back to lie along the body as the bird plunges in. The bill and skull lead the bird into the water and these are especially strong in order to absorb the impact of striking the water at high speed. The nostrils have small bony flaps which automatically shut as the bird enters the water, so stopping water being forced into the lungs. Once beneath the surface the gannet swims with strong thrusts of its feet and beats of half-opened wings in pursuit of fish.

1: Darter.
2: Dalmatian Pelican.
3: Pied Cormorant.
4: Brown Pelican.
5: Atlantic Shag.
6: Red-billed Tropic Bird.
7: Red-footed Booby.
8: Blue-footed Booby.

Having caught its victim, the gannet gulps down the fish before returning to the surface, so that other birds are unable to rob it of its kill. After a brief rest, the bird takes to the air again, circling up to reach diving height as quickly as possible. The hunting routine then begins again. A flock of over a hundred gannet wheeling, diving and climbing is an unforgettable sight and impresses all those who witness it.

For nesting sites, gannets tend to choose isolated rocky islands and precipices, though these are rarely as remote as the nesting grounds of the tropic birds. Thousands upon thousands of nesting pairs cover the ground at these locations. Each pair sits on a single egg laid on a scrappy pile of seaweed, moss and twigs which they defend violently against other birds. The nests are added to each

Top: An Australian gannet chick waits patiently on a rocky coast in New Zealand for its parents to return with food. Above: A brown pelican in the Florida Everglades.

year, with fresh material being piled on top of the old. Some nests reach a quite considerable size.

As with the pelican chicks, the single gannet young hatches as a blind and naked individual which is quite helpless. The parents feed it by dribbling regurgitated, semi-digested fish into its beak. After about three months, the chick is nearly fully grown and has acquired its full plumage, including flight feathers. At this point the adults leave the nesting grounds abandoning the chick to the elements. After several days the chicks take to the air and begin plummet-diving for fish on their own account.

The boobies are in many ways very similar to gannets. They have a similar silhouette and hunt in an almost exactly similar way. The birds are restricted to tropical and sub-tropical waters, but most species are widely distributed around the globe. The blue-footed and Peruvian boobies, however, are found only on the Pacific coast of the Americas.

These large birds took the name of booby from the fact that early mariners considered them to be remarkably stupid animals. Boobies not infrequently alighted on ships sailing the tropical waters and would then sit patiently while the sailors clubbed it and added it to the evening menu. On occasion the boobies would waddle over to the sailors as if asking to be killed. When encountered on their nesting islands, the birds were no less unsuspecting. No matter how many birds were taken, the remainder never learnt that humans were dangerous creatures. Not only was their behaviour towards man considered worthy of the name booby, but the well-known clumsiness of the birds on land made them figures of fun. When landing booby birds very often crash to the ground in a jumble of wings and legs, pitching forward on to their breasts and skidding to a halt. It is difficult to recognise the strong fliers and spectacular divers in the ungainly boobies of dry land.

The cormorants are another successful group of birds which is spread throughout the world. The great cormorant reaches three feet in length and is found on most continents. It hunts fish by diving beneath the surface in search of slower swimming fish which it has a hope of capturing. The cormorants spend much time cruising the surface of rivers and lakes before suddenly ducking beneath the water and using their feet to power themselves down to depths of up to 50 feet. The rather similar blue-eyed shag is also a superb diver in its search for food.

The hunting activities of the cormorant make it disliked by the majority of fishermen, but those of China and Japan have actually found a way of benefiting from the cormorant's skill. They use the bird to catch fish for them in rivers and lakes. Cormorant fishermen usually own ten or so birds, taking all of them out on a fishing

trip. The fishing takes place at night, with lanterns attracting the fish to the boat. Each bird has a tight leather ring around the base of its throat pouch from which a leather thong runs to the boat. The bird is placed in the water and allowed to catch fish. The leather ring prevents it from swallowing its catch. The fisherman regularly hauls the birds in and empties their pouches of fish before returning them to the water. When enough fish have been caught, the neck rings are removed and the birds allowed to swallow a pouchful of fish.

Rather similar in appearance, but placed in a different family, are the darters. They have longer, more supple necks and beaks which are straight and pointed. There are only four species of darters, sometimes termed anhingas, each of which has a distinctive range within the tropics. When hunting in lakes and rivers the birds have the unusual habit of swimming with their bodies entirely submerged, but their heads and necks held clear of the water. They can be mistaken easily for a vertical stick moving swiftly across the water.

Like other birds in the order, the darters nest in large colonies, but they take more care over their nests than most. The nests are usually built in trees overhanging rivers, or at most very close to water, and consist of a circular mass of twigs lined with leaves. The chicks are born blind and naked, but quickly become feathered and develop a remarkable defence activity. When danger threatens, they scramble out of the nest to drop into the water beneath and swim away. After a few minute they emerge from the water and climb back to the nest.

The sixth and final family included with the pelicans is that of the frigate birds which are among the most spectacular in the group. Visually the birds may appear rather dull with brown or black plumage. However in bright sunlight the feathers have a green metallic gloss and the male has a bright red throat pouch of skin which it inflates during courtship.

Frigate birds are clumsy on land, but are superb fliers having a weight of barely 3 pounds, but a wingspan of over seven feet. The birds are expert gliders and can manoeuvre with amazing agility. They take most of their food from the surface of the sea, snapping up young turtles, surface-feeding fish, floating debris and anything else which takes their fancy. They are famous for their other mode of feeding, however, and it was from this that they gained their name. In the days of sail, frigates were small, fast and heavily armed warships used to snap up the merchant ships of the enemy and to launch raids on harbours. The frigate birds have a similar propensity for a marauding lifestyle. If a frigate bird spots another bird with a fish or morsel of food, it will attack it mercilessly until the food is dropped, the frigate bird immediately snaps up the meal, leaving the other bird in peace.

1: Frigate Bird (3).
2: Australian Gannet (7).
3: Red-tailed Tropic Bird.
4: American White Pelican.

Far left: White pelicans moving in concert through the water while feeding. Left: A male frigate bird displays his colourful throat patch.

HERONS
Stealthy Fishers

Both herons and bitterns belong to the same family and share a number of characteristics which mark them out from other birds. All species are long-legged waders equipped with long stabbing beaks with which to catch their prey. The central toe is unusual in that it carries a series of horny spike-like outgrowths which project sideways.

But possibly the most distinctive feature shared by the herons is their possession of unusual powder feathers. The feathers of other birds are grown and shed at regular intervals rather like mammalian hairs so that there is a constant coat of fresh plumage. The powder feathers, however, are different. They grow continuously, pushing up from the base so that there is a constantly lengthening series of barbs. At their upper end the feathers fray and break down as fast as they grow. The powder feathers are found in paired patches either on the breast or rump and in some species form conspicuous tufts.

The powder feathers have a very specific use for the herons, for some birds more than others. The majority of the heron diet is made up of aquatic animals such as fish and amphibians whose bodies are covered with slime or mucus to a great degree. This mucus inevitably gets on to the heron's feathers, particularly round its head and neck. If left to dry the slime would clog the feathers and destroy their water-proofing and insulating properties. As soon as they have finished a meal, therefore, the birds rub any affected areas with the fine dust from the powder feathers. This soaks up the mucus and can then be cleaned out. The bitterns are particularly adept at this, perhaps because their diet includes more mucus-covered fish than does that of other herons. So vigorously do they dust themselves that they often appear to have a soft, downy appearance to their heads and breasts.

The bitterns are generally smaller than herons and are famous for their mating calls which can be heard in spring. At this time of year bitterns are more often heard than seen, only the series of croaks, booms and rattling calls which echo across the marshes giving away their presence.

The ease with which bitterns merge into their background is due to camouflage plumage and to the behaviour of the birds when threatened. Most species have striped markings on their throats and chests. When danger threatens the bitterns lift their heads to point at the sky and freeze. In this position the stripes merge with the reeds and rushes amongst which the birds live and render them almost invisible.

Other members of the family rely on flight rather than camouflage to escape predators. The grey heron is typical in that when startled it instantly takes to the air and flees with powerful strokes of its wings. It is typical of many herons in other ways too. Its chest is adorned with prominent tufts of powder feathers and it carries its neck in a characteristic S-shape. This latter feature is due to the fact that a heron's neck vertebrae are of unequal length.

When hunting the heron stands motionless in the shallows, waiting for an unsuspecting fish to come within striking range of its bill. As soon as success seems possible, the heron flings its head forward, the S-shaped neck rapidly straightening to plunge the beak into the water. The long bill closes over the prey and plucks it from the water. The hapless fish is then tossed to put it into a head-down position and swallowed.

Such a method of catching prey is common to many herons which spend their time slowly wading through shallow water or standing motionless on the bank. A notable exception is the black heron of sub-Saharan Africa. When stalking through the shallow water of swamps and marshes, the bird will repeatedly stop and bring its wings forward to form an umbrella shape over its head. Researchers are not certain why the bird does this. Perhaps the likeliest explanation is the wings create a patch of shaded water which is easier to see through than water open to the dazzling African sun. Whether or not this is the purpose of the umbrella habit, it is certainly a successful hunting ploy.

Perhaps the most spectacular herons are the egrets which are found in many areas of the world. The long, showy feathers which the egrets can boast, particularly during the breeding season are fine and spectacular. During the last century they were highly prized as fashion plumes and several species of egret were pushed close to extinction. However, conservation measures have saved them from this fate. All eight species are snowy white in colour, though the cattle egret has patches of pale yellow feathers.

The cattle egret is unusual in its feeding habits too. In addition to frequenting shallow water in search of fish and amphibians, the cattle egret haunts open plains. Here it follows cattle and other grazers and is able to pounce on insects stirred up by the large mammals.

1: Grey Heron (2).
2: Black Heron.
3: Cattle Egret.
4: Purple Heron.
5: Black-headed Heron.
6: Snowy Egret.
7: Squacco Heron.
8: Little Bittern.
9: Bittern.

Above: A cattle egret which took its name from its habit of following cattle and other large herbivores in order to snap up the insects disturbed by the mammals.

STORKS AND IBISES
Tall and Elegant

Like their close relatives, the herons, storks are tall birds with long legs and elongated bills. They are, however, much less aquatic in their habits and are often found many miles from open water. The most terrestrial of all is probably the adjutant stork or marabou of tropical Africa and India. This 5 foot tall bird is at home on the arid plains of East Africa. It feeds chiefly on carrion, being a familiar sight alongside vultures at abandoned lion kills and other carcasses. In recent years the marabou stork has been increasingly seen in towns and cities. It has adapted its carrion-eating activities to feeding on refuse tips and in the streets. Perhaps because it helps clear up organic refuse which would otherwise turn putrid in the tropical heat, the maribou is not hunted for its plumage, as are other storks.

Like its vulture companions, the maribou is notoriously ugly. Its head and neck are bare of feathers and it has a warty complexion. In addition to this there is a heavy pendant of flesh dangling from the lower throat which is similarly bare and rough. The function of the pendant is unclear, but air passages pass through it so it may be part of the respiration system.

The alternative name of the marabou, that of adjutant stork, was given to it by European settlers towards the end of last century. The bird has a stiff, stalking gait which reminded the settlers of the adjutant officers most of them had encountered at one time or another. The ugliness of the bird added barb to the comparison.

Also inhabiting tropical Africa is the saddle-billed stork, but it is rarely seen alongside the marabou for the two birds prefer very different habitats. While the marabou is a creature of the open plains, the saddle-billed stork much prefers the swamps. Particularly found in the mighty Okavango Swamp of southern Africa, the saddle-billed stork is one of the most spectacular of its group. Not only is it large, having a wingspan approaching 9 feet, but it is strikingly marked. The body is snow white with black wings and back, while the neck and head are also jet black. It is the bill, however, which is so striking. Its deep red colour is broken by a black band which runs right around it near the base and by a flap of bright yellow skin which rests over its root. It is this flap which has given the stork its name for it is shaped rather like a hunting saddle.

Similarly aquatic in habits is the wood stork of the New World. Found throughout the warmer areas of Central and South America, it is also at home in Florida. Here large breeding colonies are established each year deep within the Everglades. As many as 3,000 nests may be built together in a small clump of cypress trees, each occupied by an adult on the nest. The other parent is usually feeding in the shallow water nearby. Stirring up the mud with their feet the wood storks rely on being able to grab any creature which they disturb before it can escape.

Related to the storks are the spoonbills which are found in the warmer areas of the world. As their name suggests the spoonbills have curiously shaped bills. These are long and thin, but widen out spectacularly near the tip to form broad, rounded plates. When feeding the spoonbill moves slowly and gracefully through shallow water with its bill sweeping constantly from side to side.

Left: A painted stork alights on a waterside tree in Bharatpur in India. Below: A beautifully plumaged white ibis.

This allows the water to flow between the flattened plates, bringing with it a number of small creatures. These the spoonbill eagerly snaps up, be they fish, worms or crustaceans.

The white spoonbill of the Old World is found in some areas of southern Europe, but is more familiar in Africa. The closely related roseate spoonbill of the New World has a similar latitudinal distribution. It is often found in Florida, Louisiana and other southern states of the USA, but is more at home in South America. This species has been heavily hunted this century not only for its magnificent plumage but also for its flesh.

A similar fate has overtaken the scarlet ibis of South America. Early this century many thousands of these birds could be seen flying together over the wetlands of the lower Amazon and Orinoco. Its magnificent plumes made it much sought after for the fashion trade while its flesh is counted a delicacy by locals. Intensive hunting has severely reduced the numbers of this bird to be seen, though protected breeding grounds are helping the species survive. Another species of ibis suffered for very different reasons many centuries ago. The sacred ibis was hunted mercilessly in ancient Egypt for it was considered holy in one of the many cults of that civilisation. Thousands of the birds were caught and mummified as a ritual act, their remains still being one of the most common archaeological finds in some areas of Egypt.

1: Wood Stork.
2: Black-necked Stork.
3: Scarlet Ibis.
4: Marabou Stork.
5: Saddle-billed Stork.
6: Painted Stork.
7: Spoonbill.
8: Straw-necked Ibis.

DUCKS
Dabblers and Divers

The ducks are possibly the most familiar water birds to most people. The many species of duck share a number of features and all belong to the family anatidae. That, however, is about all that can be said with certainty about the relationships of the various species. There are around 120 species of duck which may be separated into diving ducks, dabbling ducks, freshwater ducks, sea ducks and a host of other divisions. Exactly how these are related to each other is unclear. Some ducks apparently close turn out to be morphologically different, while others at first sight distinct may be very closely related. Naturalists themselves disagree about the details of the complex relationships within the duck family, though future research may show up the true picture in time.

Among the many features which are common to all ducks are several concerned chiefly with their method of feeding. Though some ducks are aberrant, the majority feed in water by a variant of filter feeding. They may take water plants or aquatic insects, or even larger animals, but the basic feeding mechanism is very similar. The bills of ducks are broad and fairly long and have an interior fringed with tiny plates. The bill is dipped into the water and filled by the tongue which pulls sharply back, sucking water in through the plates. Larger particles in the water are excluded by the plates. When the tongue moves forward the water is pumped out, trapping the smaller particles within. The sensitive tongue sorts out the edible objects from the inedible, and positions them for swallowing.

In order to reach this food, the ducks need to swim and their legs show special adaptations to this mode of locomotion. The three forward toes are webbed, giving them a firmer purchase on water and enabling the bird to swim more powerfully and manoeuvre more delicately with less muscular effort. The legs also tend to be positioned towards the rear of the body, though not so far as in divers. While this makes for better swimming abilities, it renders the ducks rather ungainly on land and creates the familiar waddling gait.

The aquatic lifestyle also demands waterproof plumage. If the feathers were not water resistant they would quickly become waterlogged, dragging the bird down in the water and possibly leading to death by drowning. At the least the insulating properties of the feathers would be lost and the bird would suffer from cold. To keep the feathers waterproof ducks have a special gland near the tail which produces an oily secretion. When preening the ducks rub their beaks on the gland and then spread the secretion around their feathers. It is this which makes the plumage so resistant to water and gives rise to the phrase 'like water off a duck's back'.

The shoveller duck is found on wetlands throughout much of the northern hemisphere. The distinctive plumage with its bright green head and white body is restricted to the male. The female is much duller in colouration, a difference between the sexes which is found in many species of duck. Most ducks moult their flight feathers in one go in the late summer. This enables them to enjoy full flight potential for most of the year, but grounds them for three weeks while new plumage grows. At such a time the males tend to lose their gaudy feathers in favour of more sober colours.

The common mallard, found near water in the northern temperate lands, also shows a marked difference between the male with its bright plumage and the dull brown female. This species is particularly familiar to humans as the birds have learnt to tolerate human interference and so have taken well to ponds and lakes in towns and cities. The pintail duck shares much of the range of the mallard, but it has been less successful in adapting to the presence of humans. The long sharp tail of the male makes it unmistakable. Similarly distinctive is the colouration of the male tufted duck which is found through northern Europe and Asia. Its white flanks and deep purple head contrast with the brown-black body. When feeding, the tufted duck dives completely beneath the surface, swimming down with determined strokes to crop waterweeds and molluscs from the muddy bottom of the ponds or streams on which it lives. A group confined to the tropics are the whistling ducks which are sometimes termed tree ducks from their habit of roosting high in trees at night. Like other ducks they feed chiefly in the water, coming down in large flocks during the day.

1: *Northern Shoveller Duck.*
2: *Canvas-backed Duck.*
3: *Tufted Duck.*
4: *Pintail Duck.*
5: *Black-bellied Whistling Duck.*
6: *Wood Duck.*
7: *Mallard.*

Left: A female mallard duck surrounded by her chicks. The male abandons the female soon after eggs are laid and she cares for the chicks by herself. Below: A finely marked wood duck in California.

GEESE
Aggressive but Domestic

Geese are possibly the most familiar domestic fowl after the chicken and a great number of legends and tales have grown up around them. Possibly the most famous concerns the siege of Rome by Gauls in 390BC. As the siege reached its climax only the Capitol Hill remained uncaptured, and the Gauls attempted to take it by a surprise attack. They crept up the precipitous slopes at dead of night, escaping the attention of guards and dogs alike. At the very spot where the Gauls attempted to enter the fortifications, the Romans had placed the sacred geese of the goddess Juno. These geese objected to being disturbed in their sleep and called loudly. The noise alerted a Roman named Marcus Manlius who hurried to the spot and threw the Gauls back down the slope. Thereafter the sacred geese became even more favoured at Rome and geese were often employed as guards.

A less well-known goose story states that Queen Elizabeth I of England was dining off a roast goose at her Michaelmas dinner when news was brought to her that the fleeing remains of the Spanish Armada was being wrecked in storms off Scotland and Ireland. She immediately declared that she be served goose every Michaelmas to commemorate the event.

In later years goose became more famous as a Christmas dish than for Michaelmas. The geese were bred in wetland areas, in England these being the East Anglian fens, and driven to towns and cities in the autumn. There they were fattened up before being slaughtered for Christmas.

These domestic geese were descended from the greylag goose which is native to much of northern Europe and Central Asia. Reaching around 3 feet in length these are fairly big birds and consume large quantities of water weed, grass and grain. The geese pair for life and guard their nest vigorously, the trait which saved Rome. The male will drive off any intruders with much hissing and wing beating. When successful he utters a strident cry and hastens back to his mate on the nest to assure himself that all is well.

Another extremely familiar species is the Canada goose which, as its name suggests, is native to northern North America. It is to be found in many habitats, be it forest, prairie or tundra so long as there is open water nearby. The distinctive markings, with the brown body, black neck and white cheek patches, make the Canada goose instantly recognisable. The flesh of this bird is both tender and tasty and it can be easily tamed. It is therefore popular as a farmyard goose as well as a bird to be hunted. Captive birds have escaped in Britain and are now well-established as a breeding species.

Equally distinctive markings are sported by the red-fronted goose which undertakes a long migration typical of many of the northern species. It spends the summer on the open tundra to the north of the Siberian tree line. The short arctic summer produces a flush or rich but temporary food, enabling the red-fronted geese to find plenty of meals for themselves and their hatchlings. When autumn draws in the birds head southward for the Caspian Sea and neighbouring lands where they wait out the chill winter weather before heading north to breed again. The snow goose of North America follows a similar pattern, breeding in the summer on the open northern tundra and flying southwards to warmer wetlands for the winter.

Above: Snow geese flying steadily southward over Sandlake National Wildlife Refuge in South Dakota during the spring migration.

A similar habit in the barnacle goose of northern Europe and Greenland led to a folk-belief which gave the bird it name. The far northern summer grounds were unknown to medieval Europeans. They saw the birds arrive in vast numbers each autumn without knowing where they came from. At the same time autumn storms washed up timbers and other sea-born debris which carried the empty shells of goose barnacles which have a goose-like profile. It was guessed that the birds had hatched out of the barnacle shells, a 'fact' which soon became established. In some areas the church even permitted the eating of barnacle geese on fast days in the belief that they were really fish.

The dark brent goose of far northern lands around the globe is fussy about its food, taking only eelgrass which grows in the saline waters of estuaries and coastal flats. The birds move in flocks, cropping the grass off close and even entering the sea in search of food. A recent decline in the amount of eelgrass in northern Europe has led to a similar collapse in brent goose numbers. The colourful Egyptian goose has been more successful.

From its native Egypt and sub-Saharan Africa it has been introduced to isolated pockets in northern Europe, including Britain.

Two geese often seen together are the white-fronted goose and the pink-footed goose. Both are large birds which share a range across much of northern Europe and northern Asia, though only the white-fronted goose is to be found in North America. Flying together in large flocks these birds often form the classic V-shaped formation of flying geese. In addition to their natural food, these species will also consume quanities of grain and other crops. When a flock sight a potential feeding area, the birds peel off and dive in a wide, spiralling descent which brings them down almost directly beneath their break off point.

1: *Red-breasted Goose.*
2: *Canada Goose.*
3: *Emperor Goose.*
4: *Snow Goose.*
5: *Brent Goose.*
6: *Barnacle Goose.*
7: *Egyptian Goose.*
8: *White-fronted Goose.*
9: *Bar-headed Goose.*
10: *Grey Lag Goose.*
11: *Pink-footed Goose.*
12: *Beau Goose.*

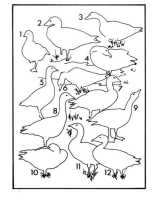

SWANS
The King's Bird

According to tradition the mute swan was brought into Britain by King Richard the Lionheart in the 1190s because he so admired its bearing and courage. Mute swans have been treated as crown property ever since and can be traded only under special license. The traditional annual ceremony of swan-upping establishes by mark the ownership of swans on the Rivers Thames and Yare. Swans were originally kept as a source of food, only later becoming the ornamental birds which they are today.

The mute swan is a large bird, measuring over five feet in length in some cases, and a powerful one. When incubating eggs, mute swans can be extremely aggressive. More than one unwary boater has found himself under attack when straying too close to a nest and some have been capsized by the angry birds. Both parents play their part in caring for the young. Before the eggs are laid, the male or cob brings suitable twigs and grass to the female, or pen, which builds it into a nest. While the pen sits on the eggs, it is the cob who guards her. Once the cygnets are hatched, the two parents shepherd them on their first journeys. Whenever alarmed, the young birds dash for the shelter of the parent birds' wings. When the cygnets lose their grey downy feathers and assume the adult plumage they leave their parents.

As its name suggests the mute swan has no voice, apart from a poor horn-like sound, but no such silence is found in other species. The whooper swan is able to produce a powerful call aptly described by the animal's name. It is found across much of northern Europe and Asia and feeds on water plants and insects like the mute swan.

The trumpeter swan is no less vocal and its voice is a rare, but insistent sound across its North American range. This bird favours standing water on open land and breeds around ponds and lakes in the northern part of the continent. During the winter flocks of these birds fly south, though do not tend to move far from the breeding grounds. These breeding grounds are today much reduced due to agriculture and the bird is found in numbers only in National Parks.

Rather more common in the New World is the whistling swan which nests on the arctic tundra around Hudson Bay and migrates many hundreds of miles in search of warmer weather when winter closes down.

The medieval chroniclers who drew up lists of beasts of the world included in their collections not only fabulous animals such as the griffin and the unicorn, but also some very garbled accounts of real animals. The lion, it was confidently asserted, had a sting in its tail like that of the scorpion. Amid these flights of fantasy there was, however, one animal which everybody agreed could not possibly exist. That creature was a black swan. When, therefore, 17th century sailors returned from the Great Southern Ocean saying that they had seen just such birds they were generally disbelieved.

There is, in fact, such a creature as a black swan thriving in Australia, but the scientists were hardly to be blamed for their mistake for, all the evidence at the time was in their favour. After all more modern scientists have refused to believe travellers' tales about creatures later proved really to exist. The swans of Europe, the only species known to science in olden times, are all white and it was unthinkable that any swan might be black. Some delicate shade of grey perhaps, but not black.

The swan which caused so much controversy, conflict and speculation is the black swan which is especially connected with the Swan River on which stands Perth, capital of Western Australia. Its colour is clearly black but the tips of its feathers are rather lighter producing a dappled effect to the plumage. It is an especially handsome bird with its brilliant red beak and large size, but is otherwise a fairly normal swan. It shares the same habits and size as its white cousins. It has been domesticated with ease and tame flocks are kept in many countries around the world.

More remarkable in colouring is the black-necked swan of the Argentine. As its name suggests this bird has a head and neck covered in black feathers, while the rest of its body is snowy white. Rather smaller than other swans, this swan ranges far and wide with breeding populations on the Falkland Islands several hundreds of miles off its continental home.

The most majestic of the white swans is undoubtedly the mute swan which is native to various isolated areas of northern Europe and central Asia. It can be easily recognised by its orange bill and the curious knob which stands at the base of its bill. The original home of the mute swan is unknown for the bird has been bred and kept in many areas for so long that it is no longer certain whether these are introduced or native populations.

Above: A black swan beating the air with its wings in the Ohau Channel of New Zealand. Left: A pair of mute swans in England. Legend long associated the beautiful but silent mute swan with a magnificent death song of unsurpassed beauty, but there is no evidence for this in fact.

1: Whooper Swan.
2: Black-necked Swan.
3: Whistling Swan.
4: Trumpeter Swan.
5: Australian Black Swan.
6: Mute Swan.

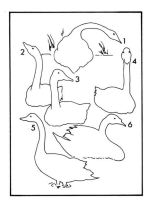

VULTURES
Watchers of the Dead

The vultures are carrion eaters of the first order which roam the skies of many areas in search of dead flesh on which to feast. They are generally large birds, with long wings for effortless, soaring flight. Some species are particularly adept at cruising thousands of feet above the ground for hours on end. Their eyesight is proverbially acute and they can spot a potential meal from a great distance. Scent may also play a part in locating the dead and the dying.

Having identified a victim the vulture turns toward the meal, losing height as it approaches. If the carcass is unavailable for some reason, perhaps the victorious predator is still feasting, the birds will circle high overhead or roost in nearby trees. Once the scene is clear, the birds will drop down almost vertically to land close to the carcass. Running forward with outstretched

necks and flapping wings, the vultures start to probe for the remaining morsels of flesh.

They are particularly well adapted to dealing with the bodies of large animals. The feet of the vultures are equipped with talons with which to hold the carcass still while tearing pieces of flesh free with their powerful, hooked beaks. The head and neck of the vultures are distinctive for they are completely bare of feathers. This gives the vultures a characteristically ugly appearance to human eyes for the skin is often mottled and decorated with growths and coloured patches. This bare skin is necessary for the vultures often push their heads deep within the carcasses of their victims. If they had plumage on their heads and necks this would quickly become clogged with blood which would dry and attract insect pests. The bare skin can easily be wiped clean.

When on a kill vultures squabble with each other constantly for the tastiest morsels. They have even been known to risk the wrath of a lion by snatching titbits of meat before the monarch of the plains has eaten his fill. So efficient are vultures at finding victims and so insistent at moving in that they have repeatedly caused problems for humans. Any hunter wishing to convert an antelope into biltong, or sun-dried meat, needs to keep the vultures at bay or he would find his entire supply filched. More gruesome is the fact that during the Boer War of 1899-1901 which was fought on the open veldt of South Africa it became accepted practice for there to be frequent truces and cease-fires so that the dead and wounded could be cleared away before the vultures arrived.

Though they share many characteristics in common, vultures are actually divided into two distinct and very different families. The vultures of the New World belong to the family cathartidae which shows certain characteristics which may link it to the stork and heron. The vultures of Africa are placed in the family accipitridae and are closely related to the hawks and eagles.

The New World vultures include the larger species, which are some of the biggest flying birds in the world. The extremely rare Californian condor can have a wingspan of around 9 feet and weigh up to 30 pounds. Such a great bird makes an impressive sight in flight, but it is not often seen. Not only is it excessively rare, with perhaps only 50 left alive, but it makes its home in the inaccessible high mountains. Here it soars effortlessly on its great wings, making use of thermals and deflected winds to keep itself airborne. One condor was once watched while it travelled over 10 miles without once flapping its wings. On good thermal days these birds probably need only flap their wings on take off. They seek out carcasses of large mammals, particularly deer, and have been known to feast on domestic stock.

Rather smaller, but still a large bird, the king vulture is found on the open pampas and in the tropical forests of Central America. The species is famed for the grotesque wattles and fleshy growths which adorn its head. The purpose of these growths is unclear but as they are not present in juveniles they may be connected with courtship in some way.

Turkey vultures range further than other New World species, being at home in a variety of habitats in both the American continents. It will eat almost anything which is left lying in sight and has been known to consume over-ripe fruit with as much relish as scraps of meat. It will even eat sealion droppings when they are available.

The griffon vulture and eared vulture are typical vultures of the African plains, though the former may be found in India and southern Europe as well. Both are fairly conventional vultures not only in appearance but also in habits. More unusual is the Egyptian vulture of India, the Middle East and the Nile Valley. This bird features on many ancient Egyptian paintings in the form of an anthropomorphic god. It is atypical in having a feathered neck and head and eating a novel diet. At carcasses, the Egyptian vulture takes only scraps discarded by others. It has, however, developed the ability to crack open eggs using stones as hammers. It is thus one of the very few birds to use a tool.

1: *Black Vulture.*
2: *Turkey Vulture.*
3: *Californian Condor.*
4: *King Vulture.*
5: *Eared Vulture.*
6: *Griffon Vulture.*
7: *Egyptian Vulture.*

Left: A young griffon vulture. This species has a wider distribution than most being found around carcasses as far afield as the African veldt and the Himalayas.

EAGLES
Kings of the Birds

The eagles are the most majestic and impressive birds in the world. Armed with sharp talons and curved beaks eagles are able to tackle a wide variety of prey, mostly small mammals. Plunging down from on high, the eagles seize their prey in their clawed feet and carry it away to some isolated crag before eating it. The name eagle is given to very different birds in different countries. Some are small, others large, but they all share the features of being active hunting birds with the female being larger than the male.

The splendid bearing of the eagles has ensured them a place in the human imagination. The folklores and mythologies are filled with supernaturally powerful eagles, even eagle gods all of which embody the strength, vitality and courage which the birds exhibit. Representations of these birds have also been used to symbolise these qualities, particularly in heraldry. The legions of Imperial Rome carried golden eagle standards into battle and their loss was as much a religious as a military disaster. Napoleon equipped his regiments with similar eagle standards to which were attached embroidered tricolours. The Austrian Empire was symbolised by a double-headed eagle, while the modern United States has as its symbol the bald eagle.

The birds which have given rise to these stories and symbolism belong to the same family as Old World vultures but are placed in the sub-family Accipitrinae, sometimes termed the Buteoninae. Within this subfamily are several genera and many species of which the most impressive is the golden eagle which may be found in remote areas through much of the northern hemisphere. It frequents mountainous areas where it can be safe from human interference. It hunts by patrolling the skies on its 6 foot wings, scanning the ground below for a potential victim. When a rodent or small bird is spotted, the eagle partially folds its wings and drops from the sky at speeds approaching 100 miles per hour. Landing on the prey with a powerful impact, the eagle pins it to the ground before flying off with it. Golden eagles have been blamed for carrying off human babies left momentarily unguarded and several apparently reliable reports of this exist. The golden eagle will also take carrion, feeding particularly on the carcasses of hill sheep.

One of the more unusual eagles is the bataleur of East Africa, its very name giving a clue to its idiosyncratic behaviour for bataleur means clown. Most of the time the bataleur behaves much like any other eagle. It flies high above the open savannah which is its home, constantly scanning the ground for the small game, especially snakes, on which it feeds. It has developed the trick of looking behind it, to catch game which is on the move in the belief that the danger is past. Occasionally, the bataleur will break this flight pattern to tumble and spin a great distance before recovering and continuing the hunt. Exactly why it indulges in this behaviour is unknown. In captivity bataleur have been observed to spread their wings, wave a clenched foot in the air utter a loud shriek and then bang their beaks against a branch. Again the reason for this behaviour is obscure.

Less unusual is the short-toed eagle of southern Europe and North Africa. It has a mottled chest, rather like the New World species known as the ornate hawk-eagle.

However, the latter also sports a stiff crest of feathers projecting from the back of it head to help account for its name. The ornate hawk-eagle lives in Central and South America.

The bald eagle, sometimes referred to as the American Eagle, has shared the fate of many eagles in recent years. It has declined in numbers, this has been largely due to the spread of human occupation which introduces agricultural chemicals to the food chain and rob the bald eagle of feeding and breeding grounds. Five centuries ago the bald eagle nested and lived throughout North America and was one of the most striking and impressive features of the American fauna to greet the first European settlers. It has now been driven from most of its range. Breeding populations of any size are found only in Florida and Alaska, and even in the former, numbers have declined recently.

The birds feed chiefly on fish, preferring to take the dead or dying when they can, but will hunt small mammals and birds on occasion. During the annual salmon run, the bald eagle of the west coast find food easily. The fish swim up the rivers which empty into the Pacific in huge numbers and, once they have spawned, they die. The river banks become littered with dead fish on which the bald eagles feast. At other times of the year the bald eagle actively hunts fish. It patrols lakes and ponds watching for a fish to surface. Diving steeply down, the eagle levels out at the last moment allowing its claws to snatch at the fish without entering the water itself.

1: Wedge-tailed Eagle.
2: Verraux's Eagle.
3: Bataleur Eagle.
4: Long-crested Eagle.
5: Ornate Hawk Eagle.
6: Bald Eagle.
7: Martial Eagle.
8: Golden Eagle.
9: Short-toed Eagle.

Left: A bald eagle grasping a salmon. Though able to catch live fish from the water, the bald eagle prefers to scavenge for dying fish floating on the surface.

FALCONS
Birds of Sport

Unlike the diverse hawks, the 60 or so species of falcon belong to a single taxonomic family, the falconidae, with clearly defined borders and characteristics. All falcons have feathered thighs and bare shins and feet. They have long narrow wings which end in distinct points, and most have a clear notch on their beaks. All falcons are fast-flying daytime hunters which actively pursue their prey. Falcons do not build nests, instead they either lay their eggs on the ground or take over abandoned nests of other species.

The speed and tenacity of the falcon in the hunt was the basis for the old aristocratic sport of falconry which was once so popular in Europe and Asia. Falcons, of various species, were caught when still young and trained to be domesticated hunting birds. They were schooled to return to the handler when called by offering them rewards of food. The birds, however, never lost their hunting instinct and were used to bring down game birds.

The noblemen, or women, rode out to likely hunting grounds with the falcon perched on their hands, suitably covered with leather gauntlets. The birds wore hoods which covered their eyes so that they would not be distracted by surrounding activity. The ground would be beaten and when a game bird was started the falcon's hood was removed and it was sent in pursuit of its prey. For centuries the sport was highly popular and good falcons were worth considerable sums of money. The sport is still popular in some eastern nations, but has almost vanished in Europe. The advent of a reliable and accurate hunting gun made the use of falcons unnecessary.

Possibly the favourite bird for falconry training is the peregrine falcon and the reason is not difficult to deduce. When hunting the peregrine puts on one of the finest and most impressive displays of any bird of prey. It climbs rapidly to a height of around 1,000 feet where it circles and quarters the air in search of a victim. When a flock or a single bird comes into sight, the peregrine carefully positions itself above and behind the potential prey. It then launches a spectacular attack, the tactics of which would be borrowed by fighter pilots in the First World War.

The peregrine drops its head and folds its wings into a trailing V-shape. In this form it stoops, diving down in a near vertical dive of almost incredible speed. One bird was timed at around 180 miles per hour in a stoop. Before the victim is aware of its presence, the falcon is on top of it, bringing its taloned feet round to slam into the victim, breaking is back instantly. While the prey drops to the ground, the peregrine climbs, twisting as it does so in order to keep the prey in sight. It then drops to the ground again to begin its meal. Such a thrilling spectacle formed an exciting part of falconry.

Much more common than the peregrine, particularly in Europe, is the kestrel. This rather smaller bird measure only around 13 inches in length but it is an active hunter. It sweeps across open country at a fairly low height, keeping an eager eye open for mice and other rodents scurrying through the grass and undergrowth. When it sights a potential victim the kestrel halts and hovers with rapid wing beats before dropping from the sky in a dive shorter and slower than that of the peregrine. Victims are

pinned to the ground by the clawed feet and rapidly despatched.

One of the fastest and most agile falcons is the hobby, found throughout most of Europe and Asia and in parts of North Africa. This small bird is a magnificent flier, its hunt being almost as spectacular as that of the peregrine. The hobby chases, rather than stoops, pursuing prey as swift and agile as swallows and swifts. Its long, tapering wings are reminiscent of the birds it hunts. The high speed, darting chase may involve aerobatics of a bewildering rapidity and will end when the hobby closes its claws around the victim and carries it off to a perch before eating it.

The merlin is a falcon of open heathland and is also a chasing bird. It pursues small birds such as pigeons, pipits and ouzels across the heather. The twisting, darting flight of a merlin after it prey can be dazzling to watch and the birds are easily lost to sight as they skim over and around the vegetation. In medieval European falconry the merlin was known as a lady's falcon for it is easily handled and is attractive to watch. The powerful aero engine which powered the Spitfire of World War II is named the merlin.

1: *European Kestrel.*
2: *Peregrine Falcon.*
3: *Hobby Falcon.*
4: *Merlin Falcon.*
5: *Collared Forest Falcon.*
6: *Prairie Falcon.*
7: *Crested Caracara.*

An unusual falcon is the caracara of Central America and the southern states of the USA. This bird is largely a scavenger. It spends relatively little time in the air, being often found stalking across grasslands or roads in search of carcasses upon which to feed. It is, however, no coward and will readily drive other scavengers from a carcass in order to secure the choicest pieces of flesh.

Above: A crested caracara swoops to land on a rock in the Falkland Islands. The caracara will take many types of food, from insects to carrion.

PHEASANTS
Long Tailed Game Birds

The pheasants are a group of birds spread widely through the Old World and numbering some 180 species. The group is highly diverse so that it is not always easy to recognise a pheasant. Indeed common parlance has divided the birds into a number of types, such as pheasant, peafowl and partridge, but they remain members of the same family. Though the birds are so different in appearance they do share some characteristics. The lower legs are largely free of feathers, as are the nostrils and they lack the inflatable throat pouches found in many related birds, such as the grouse.

Certainly the most visually impressive of the pheasants is the peafowl, the male of which has a stunning tail. The tail is composed of long feathers of iridescent blues and greens adorned with large yellow and black eyespots and

tipped by swallow-tail shaped tufts. When displaying to the female the peacock faces his potential mate and erects this tail to form an enormous fan behind his body. This is then shaken and shivered to allow the light to catch the delicate shimmering shades of colour. The female often displays her meagre, drab tail feathers in return, whereupon the birds mate and a primitive nest is made by scraping a slight hollow in the ground in which about 5 eggs are laid.

The peacock is native to India and Sri Lanka where it lives in forests, often near open land. The birds hide in dense cover during the day, emerging at dusk to feed on a wide variety of vegetable and animal food including insects, shoots, fruits and seeds. The sheer beauty of the

birds led to their being domesticated several thousand years ago to grace the gardens of Indian princes.

There they were encountered by Alexander the Great on his march of conquest. Alexander ordered the birds to be protected and took some breeding fowl back to Europe. The Romans, with their liking for ostentatious luxury, bred peafowl not only for decoration but also for the table. Peacocks would be roasted, allowed to cool and then dressed in their feathers before being taken to the table as a centrepiece for banquets. The practice continued long after the fall of Rome, but has now fallen from use. The species is well established in many nations as an ornamental garden bird, but has rarely had success in the wild beyond its home range.

Only slightly smaller than the 8 foot long peacock is the male argus pheasant which inhabits the forests of Southeast Asia. Though almost as large as its Indian counterpart, the argus pheasant has never been taken into captivity for its plumage is dull and drab. Only the blue neck and yellowish roundels on the extraordinarily long wing feathers adding a spark of colour.

One of the most attractive pheasants is the golden pheasant of western China. Less than half the length of the peacock, the male golden pheasant nonetheless has a fine plumage. The long tail is of speckled yellow and black feathers while the red body is decorated with splashes of yellow and blue. The head carries a crest of feathers which hangs down over the shoulders to form a distinctive cape. Golden pheasants live in dense undergrowth and when danger threatens are more likely to dash for cover than to attempt to fly away.

This shyness and liking for near-impenetrable cover has made the pheasants a peculiarly difficult group of birds to study. Indeed the habits, lifestyle and population of many species is virtually unknown. More interesting is the fact that many species were not even known to exist until this century. The existence of the mikado pheasant, for instance, was utterly unsuspected until 1900. In that year an Englishman visiting Formosa obtained two long black feathers from locals. Neither he nor any of his friends could identify the species which had produced the feathers, and their origin remained a mystery for some years until a complete specimen was obtained. The brightly coloured Sinhoe's pheasant of the same island has been equally retiring and very little is known about it.

Less retiring is the turkey which is native to much of North and Central America. The wild turkey is a creature of woodland and open scrub where it can find the seeds, berries and insects on which it feeds. Moving in small flocks, the turkeys walk steadily through the forest during daylight hours and fly up into the branches to seek roosting places for the night. They are heavy fliers and rarely travel more than a few yards on the wing.

When the Spaniards arrived in Mexico in the late 15th century they found turkeys already domesticated by the local tribes. These birds were taken back to Europe and within a few decades were firmly established as birds to be used by the nobility or on festive occasions. It was some years before selective breeding was begun on a large scale. The modern white turkey is more tender and slightly smaller than its wild counterpart and is the breed raised in most countries.

1: Argos Pheasant.
2: Mikado Pheasant.
3: Peacock.
4: Swinhoe's Pheasant.
5: Turkey.
6: Golden Pheasant.

Left: A peacock displaying his magnificent plumage. The fine feathers play an important part in the courting ritual with the colourful male showing them to the drab female in order to attract her.

WADERS
Birds of the Shore

The order of birds designated Charadriiformes is immensely diverse including many birds which, at first sight, bear little resemblance to each other. Within the group are three broad categories; the waders, the gulls and the auks, each of which has distinct features. Yet despite this apparent diversity, the Charadriiformes are a proper scientific grouping sharing a number of features which marks them off from other birds.

These similarities are largely internal including, among other things, the bones of the palate and the arrangement of leg tendons. There are, however, several behavioural traits as well. Most species are coastal in habitat, with only a very few being adapted to life inland. They tend to breed slowly but successfully. Only one batch of perhaps 3 eggs is produced annually, but there is a high rate of chick survival so that populations are kept well up.

The first and largest group of Charadriiformes are the waders, consisting of a dozen families and many species. As their name suggests these birds are adapted to life along the shore, wading through shallow water in search of food. They all have relatively long, bare legs to keep their bodies clear of the water and slender toes to help find a purchase. The bills of these birds vary enormously depending on the food which is being sought. Some have long thin beaks, others short and blunt ones and these are useful identification aids in the field.

The lapwing belongs to the plover family and is widespread across Central Asia and Europe, except Spain. It is one of the few Charadriiformes to become adapted to life spent largely on land. It is a creature of the marshes, where it stalks through the damp lands in search of insects, which it consumes in vast numbers. It is also to be found in damp meadows and on agricultural fields where it continues to snap up insects. The benefit of this behaviour to farmers has long been recognised and, in Britain, the bird has been protected for generations. On the European continent the lapwing has been less fortunate with the French in particular making use of the bird for culinary purposes. It is therefore accordingly rarer in areas where its eggs are taken or it is shot.

The lapwing is particularly noticeable in the spring when the males indulge in a spectacular courtship display. Climbing high into the sky, the bird will suddenly appear to stall and tumbles downward in a series of spins and rolls which seem to be pulling it into a destructive crash. The bird inevitably pulls out in time to climb again to repeat the manoeuvre while uttering its loud 'peewit' call, which has become another name for this bird.

The redshank has a similar geographical distribution to that of the lapwing, but is more devoted to aquatic habitats. It feeds by striding through the shallow, muddy waters on the shores of ponds and lakes or along the banks of rivers. Here the redshanks find various invertebrates, including worms and insects on which they feast. Like the lapwing, the male redshank has a courtship display but it is much less spectacular. He will dash around, often chasing a female, with his tail spread out in a fan.

The common snipe can be readily identified by its long, straight bill. Its range includes most of Europe and northern Asia as well as North America and parts of

Africa and South America. The long bill is essential to the snipe's style of feeding. The upper bill is slightly longer than the lower and bulges near the tip. The lower bill fits snugly behind the bulge and is thus protected when the bill is pushed into the earth. The tips of the bills are flexible and highly sensitive. When a worm is sensed, the bill is opened and the worm gripped. When startled the snipe flies low and fast, zig-zagging with almost incredible agility. As one huntsman is said to have reported in despair of a snipe 'When I shot zig it flew zag, and when I shot zag it flew zig'.

The delicate avocet is one of the birds which has experienced a comeback in the 20th century. A late 19th century British nature book dismissed the bird with the words 'Formerly breeding here, but now only a visitor'. Today small breeding populations are established in East Anglia, and similar increases have been reported elsewhere in the avocet's range which reaches across Eurasia to northern China. The curious upturned beak of this bird is used to hunt out the shrimps and water insect larvae on which it feeds. The nests are built beside water as untidy piles of aquatic plants and usually hold four eggs which hatch in June.

The oystercatcher is a familiar creature of the seashore with its bold black and white plumage and red bill. It hunts through the shallows for marine worms and molluscs the shells of which it prises apart before consuming the soft body within.

Very different is the stonecurlew with its short, stumpy bill which is used not so much for probing muddy waters as for catching insects, frogs and other small animals. This bird is to be found across much of Europe, southern Asia and North Africa, migrating to the southern parts of its range in the winter. It takes its name from its habit of nesting on stony ground where it scrapes a small hollow in which to lay just 2 eggs.

1: *Red Shank.*
2: *Avocet.*
3: *Common Sandpiper.*
4: *Oystercatcher.*
5: *Black-tailed Godwit.*
6: *Curlew.*
7: *Stone Curlew.*
8: *Lapwing.*

Left: An American avocet standing motionless above its own reflection. It searches for water insects and other small creatures with its upswept bill.

GULLS
Opportunist Sea Birds

The second large grouping of Charadriiformes is that of the gulls which includes three families, the skuas, the true gulls and the skimmers. These birds are typically marine with webbed feet and slightly hooked beaks which feed on a wide variety of foods to be found at sea or along the shore. Some species are found far inland where they have learnt to take a wide variety of food.

Though many species in this group are persistent and aggressive birds, the skuas are more belligerent than most. They are powerful with strongly hooked beaks and great flying ability. They are sometimes known as jaegers, derived from the German word for hunter which is an apt description of their behaviour.

Rather than find their own food the skuas have developed a tactic for robbing other birds of their meals. When they come upon another bird with a fish in its mouth, the skuas will dive to the attack. They chase the other bird, harrying it mercilessly until it drops its load. The skuas then dive on the fish, snapping it up quickly. Skuas will also attack unladen gulls, taking advantage of the gulls' habit of regurgitating their last meal when frightened in order to lighten their bodies and so increase their air speed. When the gull discards its meal the skua drops down to secure it.

Skuas will also rob the nests of other seabirds. Often the skuas act in pairs when after eggs or chicks. The first makes a diversionary attack, drawing off the parent birds. Meanwhile the second skua dashes in to seize the eggs or chicks and make off before the parents realise what is happening.

The Arctic skua, sometimes called the parasitic jaegar, is some 18 inches in length and may be found around many coasts in the far northern oceans. It is often sighted at sea, harrying other seabirds for their food, but nests inland on open moorland where it lays 2 eggs in a grass-lined hollow in the ground. The rather similar long-tailed skua inhabits the same type of range. It can be readily recognised by the pair of long straight feathers feathers which project from its tail. In the autumn the long-tailed skua leaves the far northern waters, but nobody is entirely certain where they go. The best guess is that they retreat to oceanic regions further south.

The gulls and terns both belong to the Laridae family, though there are several differences between them. Gulls are large birds with webbed feet. They are superb fliers and can soar and glide for long periods with no need for active flight. They feed on a variety of food, some concentrating on fish, but other species will rob nests or relish carrion and refuse. Because of these preferences gulls have become perhaps the best known of seabirds. They frequent fishing ports in search of discarded fish entrails and flesh and are numerous around coastal towns where they find much food in refuse tips. Some gulls have moved inland in search of similar sources of food, particularly in the colder months when they may have difficulty finding food at sea. Despite the fact that many people believe the gulls to be marine birds, they are actually coastal creatures which rarely wander more than a few hours flight from shore. It is their raucous presence at seaside towns which have fixed them in the popular mind as oceanic birds.

Most species nest together in large colonies which can be extremely noisy. Thousands of birds gather together to lay two or three eggs in small, primitive nests. After hatching the young are fed by their parents for a month or so until they can fly, when they are abandoned.

The herring gull is limited to North America and western Europe but is very numerous within this range. It is fairly large, measuring nearly 2 feet in length, and is a powerful flier. It will eat almost anything which comes its way and has become a successful scavenger on town dumps. It is the loud yelping of this bird which is familiar to many holidaymakers. The Straits of Gibralter seem to form an effective barrier to the bird, for its cries are only common west of Gibralter.

Below: A pair of great black-backed gulls with a mottled chick. Bottom: An Arctic tern skimming over the Farne Islands. This bird has the longest migration route of any animal, flying from Arctic to Antarctic feeding grounds.

1: Herring Gull.
2: Long-tailed Skua.
3: Great Black-backed Gull.
4: Black Tern.
5: Arctic Tern.
6: Common Tern.
7: Arctic Skua.
8: Black-headed Gull.

The smaller black-headed gull has moved inland to town refuse tips alongside the herring gull, but it can also be seen following ploughs waiting for the machines to turn up invertebrates. During the winter it loses its black head plumage in favour of speckled white and brown. The much larger great black-backed gull is more restricted to the coast. It is a powerful bird with a sharp bill with which it will rob nests, attack other birds or swoop down on any offal it can reach.

Smaller and more graceful, the terns are adapted to oceanic flight. They spend most of their lives aloft, only coming to ground to breed and rarely resting on the water. They feed by diving at fish from a height, and swooping up after seizing the victim in their beaks. Most terns are fairly similar in appearance, with a snow white body and coal black cap, though the black tern has a grey body and charcoal wings.

AUKS
Arctic Auks

The third major division of the Charadriiformes is that of the auks. There are fewer species of auks than of gulls or waders, there being only 22 world wide. They are generally small birds with plumage which is sharply broken into a dark back and pale underparts. It is a feature they share with the penguins, and there are other similarities as well. Both groups are largely restricted to polar seas, with the penguins in the Antarctic and the auks in the arctic. Both groups spend much of their time swimming on the surface of the sea and dive beneath the surface to hunt small fish. Once beneath the surface both groups swim by 'flying' through the water with their short, narrow wings.

That is as far as the similarity goes for in truth the two groups are not at all closely related. The resemblances are due to the fact that both have evolved to suit much the same lifestyle, not to any close kinship. The auks, unlike the penguins, can fly, though their agility in the air is poor and no match for their powers beneath the waves.

The distinctive features of the auks were taken to extremes by the great auk, which is now extinct. This bird measured 30 inches in length and was completely unable to fly. It spent the vast majority of its life swimming the seas, ranging from within the Arctic Circle to the Caribbean. Each summer the birds scrambled ashore on islands of the North Atlantic from Greenland to Scandinavia to mate and lay their eggs. The great auk was not only unable to fly but was even clumsier on land than its surviving relatives. Early sailors looked on the huge rookeries as an easy source of much needed fresh meat and slaughtered the birds by the thousand whenever the opportunity offered. The last known pair were killed in 1844 on an island off the Icelandic coast.

In contrast to its unfortunate relative the little auk is one of the most numerous birds on earth. This bird is barely 8 inches long and is able to fly, but otherwise shares many of habits of the great auk. It is restricted to the North Atlantic and spends much of its time at sea, only coming ashore to breed on small islands scattered around the chill Arctic Ocean. The breeding colonies are large and noisy, with several thousand of these little birds packed together in a small area, often on rocky shores and cliff edges. Usually only one egg is laid, which hatches within a month to produce a chick which takes to the water quickly.

So common are the little auks that they form a staple diet of many eskimo tribes during the weeks they are ashore. The birds are caught in devices rather like large, tough butterfly nets after being started from their nests by a loud noise. Their oily, fishy flesh is treated as something of a delicacy.

Only slightly larger are the crested auklet and the whiskered auklet. Both these species take their names from their showy breeding plumage. The whiskered auklet grows a bright white chevron of feathers between its bill and its eye. The upper branch of the chevron being formed by a tuft which rises above the head. The bill of the crested auklet, like that of the whiskered auklet changes from dull beak to brilliant red for the breeding season ashore and grows a curving, feathering plume of black feathers which springs from the base of its bill and turns forward. It is restricted to the northern Pacific and the Bering Sea.

The razorbills and guillemots, or murres, are the largest existing auks, with the common guillemot topping 16 inches in length. These birds tend to be more graceful than other auks with more slender bodies and longer bills. Guillemot nesting grounds are the subject of sustained attacks by egg-stealing and chick hunting gulls so the auks spend as little time as possible ashore. They do not build a nest, but lay the egg directly on to a rocky ledge. The eggs pear shaped, which may mean that it rolls in a circle around its narrower end rather than off the ledge. Within two weeks of hatching the young have acquired their adult plumage and take to the sea where they continue to be cared for by their parents.

Possibly the most familiar of the auks is the puffin, of which there are several species. These birds are about a foot in length and are particularly noticeable for their brightly coloured bills. These bills are grown only during the breeding season, at the onset of winter the colourful outer casing is shed. The Atlantic has only one species, the common puffin, while the more colourful tufted and horned puffins are found in the North Pacific.

Puffins nest on isolated oceanic islands, digging burrows deep beneath the soil in which a single egg is laid. Both parents incubate the egg and care for the young by bringing it fish in their mobile bills. Eventually the chick is abandoned to find its own way to the sea.

1: *Horned Puffin (4).*
2: *Little Auk (2).*
3: *Brunnich's Guillemot.*
4: *Common Guillemot (2).*
5: *Black Guillemot.*
6: *Whiskered Auklet.*
7: *Crested Auklet.*
8: *Atlantic Puffin.*
9: *Tufted Puffin.*

Far left: A horned puffin displaying its bill in breeding coloration. Left: A trio of guillemots with a pair of chicks. Guillemots gather in May to lay their single eggs on inaccessible cliffs and rocky islets.

PIGEONS
The Town Birds

Pigeons, known to science as Columbiformes, are a highly successful and widespread group of birds. Of nearly 300 species many are spread across vast areas of land and the group is found on every continent except Antarctica. The majority of species are to be found in eastern Asia and Australasia where these birds have been particularly successful at adapting to slightly different ways of life.

Physically the many different species resemble each other so closely that there is never any doubt that the bird in question is a pigeon. They are all plump, round-bodied birds with strong legs bearing four toes and which are usually partly feathered. The head is small and carries a short, rounded bill which is used to gather the seeds, fruits and grain on which these birds feed. Their vast appetites and large numbers have made these birds considerable pests when they feed on agricultural land. Farmers go to great lengths to destroy the pigeons or drive them off the land. The birds continue to take a large and expensive proportion of various crops, however.

Pigeons share broadly similar nesting practices which vary little between species or localities. A small nest of twigs is usually built in which two, or sometimes three, eggs are laid. The eggs are almost universally white and shiny, though a few species produce slightly bluish eggs. Both parents take their turns incubating the clutch, often with the female taking the night turn. They are not, however, strongly attached to the nest. They make little attempt to defend it against intruders and once frightened off rarely return. In such a case the birds will build a new nest and lay again. Even when the reproductive process is successful, the birds may build a second nest, some species producing several broods in the course of a breeding season.

The eggs hatch after only about two weeks in most species, though some take as long as a month. The chicks, or squabs as they are properly known, hatch blind and naked but within days produce their first plumage and open their eyes. The parents feed their young on a substance known as 'pigeon's milk', a nutritious white liquid produced in the bird's crop and regurgitated for the young. Within a month the squabs are fully feathered and able to care for themselves, whereupon they are abandoned by the parents.

The most familiar pigeon to many is the domestic pigeon, a variant of the rock dove. The truly wild birds are just over a foot in length and feed on grain and invertebrates. They nest on cliff ledges or in rocky crevices. These birds have colonised towns and cities around the world where they exist in large numbers and have become something of a pest, leaving their unhygienic droppings indiscriminately. The birds feed on scraps and refuse and nest on buildings whose high, vertical sides so closely resemble the cliffs of their original home. The birds are often unmolested by humans and in many areas have almost entirely lost their fear of man. The racing pigeon which is kept for sport as well as for carrying messages is a fully domesticated variety of this species.

The wood pigeon is spread through most of Europe and parts of western Asia. It is about 16 inches long and devours huge quantities of seeds and grain, particularly from arable fields. It has increased in numbers as modern farming techniques produce larger crops. This species has also moved into town parks and gardens where its soft, but monotonous, cooing has become a familiar sound.

Left: A wood pigeon on its nest. Only two eggs are laid and the parents feed the chicks on a protein- and fat-rich secretion called 'pigeon milk'.

The crested pigeon is a species of the arid regions in Australia. It moves in small groups of perhaps two dozen, but may gather in hundreds at popular waterholes. They feed on seeds of desert plants and devour green shoots at an alarming rate.

Possibly the most famous member of the columbiformes, however, is no longer in existence. This was the dodo, a well known symbol of extinction, which lived on the islands of Mauritius, Reunion and Rodriguez in the Indian Ocean. The bird was larger than a turkey and fed on fruits and leaves. It had an ungainly appearance quite unlike that of any other member of its order. The body was short and rounded while the head was large and bulbous with a bare face. The comical appearance of the bird was completed by a pair of ridiculously short wings and a tufted tail. European sailors arriving on the islands for the first time took hundreds of these flightless birds to re-stock their ships and so brought about a sharp decline in the dodo population. However, the final extinction of these birds, which varied between the islands from around 1680 to 1800, was more due to the activities of introduced wild pigs than to direct human contact.

The passenger pigeon of North America fell victim to direct human predation. This 18 inch bird once moved through the forests of the Eastern USA in vast flocks numbering millions of birds. The flocks nested together in small areas of woodland, turning the neighbourhood into a noisy, smelly mess. The flesh of the birds was extremely tasty while squabs could be caught by the hundreds of thousands at the nesting sites. By the close of the 19th century the passenger pigeon was extinct. One other species is probably extinct, but nobody can be certain. In 1904 six specimens of an entirely unknown bird were found in the Solomon Islands. It was named the little crested pigeon, but has never been seen since.

1: Wood Pigeon.
2: Olive Pigeon.
3: Two-coloured Imperial Pigeon.
4: Galapagos Dove.
5: Racing Pigeon.
6: Bar-shouldered Dove.
7: Crested Pigeon.
8: Town Pigeon.
9: Laughing Dove.

PARROTS
Colourful Talkers

The distinctive and brightly coloured parrots are possibly the only birds to become established as pets, rather than as domesticated sources of meat and eggs. Exactly when parrots were first domesticated, and where, is unknown. The earliest literary references to pet parrots come from ancient Greece, but at that time the birds were clearly unusual novelties. With the Dark Ages after the fall of Rome in the 5th century AD the parrot vanishes from written records.

The great age of pet parrots came when European seamen began exploring the globe in the 15th to 18th centuries. The sailors, ever on the lookout for an exotic curiosity to take home, fixed on the parrot as an ideal souvenir with which to return from foreign lands. So universal did the parrot become either as a shipboard pet or as a companion for a retired sailor that popular literature portrayed seamen as being constantly accompanied by parrots. Perhaps the most famous fictional character to have a pet parrot is the pirate Long John Silver from the children's novel *Treasure Island*. His shoulder was constantly occupied by a parrot named Captain Kidd which squawked, among other things, such nautical terms as 'pieces of eight'.

It was this talking ability which probably attracted early mariners to the birds. In the wild parrots are noisy birds, but have only a limited range of calls. Their screeches and squawks are a familiar sound in the tropical jungles, often carrying for some distance. However once captured, or if raised in captivity, the parrots will copy almost any sound which they hear.

Usually parrots will imitate the sounds which they hear most often. It is for this reason that parrot owners repeat the same phrase over and again to their pets in the hope that it will be picked up and become part of the bird's vocabulary. In the days when pet birds were brought to industrialised nations on board sailing ships, the sounds of a ship at sea formed a large part of any bird's vocal range. Birds could imitate almost exactly the sound of ropes running through wooden blocks, or the clanking of capstan ratchets, and so cause confusion to their land-bound owners.

Occasionally a bird will add a sound to is repertoire when it hears it only once, especially if the sound is loud and dramatic. One parrot heard a dog have its paw run over by a cart wheel and ever afterward would repeat the startled yelp of the animal, followed by a howl of pain and the fast diminishing moans as the dog ran off. Those unused to the bird were continually looking around for an injured dog. Slightly more embarrassing is when a parrot picks up a swear word, uttered loudly and with feeling in its presence, and then cheerfully repeats it to visitors.

The decline of the sailing ship late last century reduced the numbers of men needed at sea and led to a decline in the link between parrots and mariners. But by that time parrot-keeping was well established amongst landsmen and continued until the years just before the Second World War when a virulent parrot disease was identified as the cause for infection among bird owners. The trade in parrots declined and has only recently begun to recover.

The most commonly kept birds, the so called cage-parrots, come from both Africa and South America.

Perhaps the best talker, and therefore most valuable bird, is the African grey parrot from Central Africa. This bird inhabits dense forest and open scrubland right across the continent from the Congo to Mount Kilimanjaro where it feeds on nuts and berries. As its name suggests its body is an almost uniform grey, though the tail is a contrasting and startling red colour. From the New World come the various species of Amazon parrots, which take readily to human contact and speak well. The white-fronted Amazon parrot is one of the smaller species with a length of around 10 inches and a noticeable white forehead. The closely related blue-fronted Amazon parrot is also a popular cage bird.

All parrots belong to the order Psittaciformes, which contains but one family, the Psittacidae. This grouping forms a compact and neatly defined body, but within it the divisions are much less certain. Today there are generally reckoned to be 315 species of parrot, though a century ago one authority stated that 'more than 500 different species have been described'. The dramatic decline in number of species is not due to large scale exterminations and extinctions, but to the disputes within scientific circles.

Former generations of naturalists tended to recognise each different type of bird as a separate species, though the variation between it and another species might be very small. This led to a proliferation of species names. More modern scientists have decried this practice as needlessly complicated. Instead they prefer to treat minor variations on a theme as subspecies or localised races of a single species. Thus a modern 'species' might include within it several older 'species' formerly recognised as independent. This trend affects not only birds but other

1: Golden-shouldered Parrot.
2: White-fronted Amazon Parrot.
3: Electus Parrot (2).
4: Princess Parrot.
5: African Grey Parrot.
6: Hawk-headed Parrot.
7: Blue-fronted Amazon Parrot.
8: Ring-necked Lorikeet.
9: King Parrot.
10: Masked Lovebird.
11: Fischer's Lovebird.
12: White-breasted Caique.
13: Sun Conure.
14: Slate-headed Parakeet.
15: Crimson Rosella.

Left: The aptly-named rainbow lorikeet, an Australian species which flies in flocks of up to 100 birds and can do much damage to crops and orchards.

1: Palm Cockatoo.
2: Gang-Gang Cockatoo.
3: Sulphur-crested
Cockatoo.
4: Pink Cockatoo.
5: Hyacinthine Macaw.
6: Red-tailed Black
Cockatoo.
7: Long-billed Corella.
8: Pesquet's Fruit-eating
Parrot.
9: Yellow-tailed Black
Cockatoo.
10: Kea.

*Left: A red and green
macaw. Below: A blue and
yellow macaw. There are
several species of macaw,
characterised by bald faces
and they are generally known
by the colours of their
plumage.*

living animals, and the study of prehistoric creatures such as dinosaurs as well.

Uncertainty still prevails in the nomenclature of the parrots. Common parlance distinguishes between parrots, parrakeets, cockatoos, lories, macaws, budgerigars and lorikeets. The majority of these terms are of local origin and apply to various physical appearances which may have no relation to the taxonomic relationships between species. Nonetheless some authorities choose to separate some of these groupings into separate families with as much importance as the Psittacidae. The cockatoos and lories are those most often separated out into the Loriidae and Cacatuidae families respectively. Other scientists treat these merely as sub-families within the Psittacidae while a few refuse to accept their validity at all. The main difficulty is that parrots differ so markedly from other birds, yet are a particularly homogenous group themselves.

Parrots are spread right around the globe, though they are restricted to the tropical belt and are chiefly creatures of the forest, or at least scrub country. In size they range from the 3 inch red-breasted pygmy parrot of New Guinea to the macaws which may reach 3 feet in length. All parrots have large heads and short necks with sturdy bodies, often with long tail feathers. The plumage is characteristically bright and showy with many different hues, of which greens, reds, yellows and blues are perhaps the most common. The typical plumage pattern is for the body to be of one colour while the head and wings are decorated with other shades. However, some species break this trend by having brilliantly coloured splashes on almost any part of their bodies.

Like the herons, parrots have powder feathers. These are special feathers which instead of falling out and being replaced periodically in order to keep the plumage in top condition, are retained throughout the bird's life. These feathers grow continuously from the root and fray at the ends. The soft barbs and shafts break down into a dust-like powder. This is used by the bird when preening rather like blotting paper. It soaks up any liquids or soft fruit pulp which have become trapped in the feathers, and can then be preened out with ease. Unlike the herons, which have conspicuous paired tufts of powder

feathers on their chests, the parrots have powder feathers spread evenly throughout the body.

In addition to this distinctive plumage, parrots also have a common pattern of absence of feathers. They have patches of bare skin around the eyes, though this varies in size from species to species and may be almost undetectable. More obvious is the flap of skin, called a cere, which covers the base of the upper bill and through which the nostrils open. In many other birds the nostrils open directly through the bill.

The bill of the parrots is a unique organ quite unlike that of any other type of bird and one the group's most distinctive features. Both the upper and lower bills are sharply hooked, but in opposite directions so that the lower bill fits snugly inside the much larger and broader upper bill when the beak is closed. Uniquely the upper bill is not fixed rigidly to the skull, but is jointed so that it can move in relation to the lower mandible much more accurately and delicately than can those of other birds. This is of particular importance when considering the food preferred by parrots which often needs peeling or shelling before it can be consumed. Within the beak is a muscular tongue which further aids the manipulation of food items.

But it is not merely the beak which plays a role in feeding, the feet too are of crucial importance. The feet of the parrot are strong and capable of grasping even the smallest objects. They are four-toed with two toes pointing forward and the other pair backwards giving a near perfect opposable grip. Most parrots will balance on one leg when feeding. The second limb is used to hold a piece of food while the bill works at it. In captivity parrots often use this technique to shell and eat groundnuts.

Parrots do not use their impressive dexterity with legs and beak only for feeding. They live largely in forest or scrub habitats and are skilled climbers. Their feet are ideally shaped for gripping twigs and branches and allow parrots to shuffle along branches with ease. When faced with a vertical climb up a tree the parrot will grip the trunk with its bill and then hoist its body up, hold itself with its feet while shifting the bill to a spot higher up the trunk and begin the process again.

One species of parrot which has taken the use of it feet and bill to an extreme is the kakapo of New Zealand.

This bird has entirely abandoned flight in favour of it climbing abilities, which have become improved and refined. Using its bill and legs it can climb easily through the dense upland forests which are its home. The male kakapo has a loud, booming courtship call which resounds through the forests. When a mate has been attracted the pair dig a burrow in which a single or pair of eggs are laid and where the chick is cared for.

The kakapo has been able to abandon flight because of the lack of terrestrial carnivores on New Zealand. The island group was cut off from the rest of the land masses of the world before either mammals or birds evolved. Only those animals able to swim or fly across the ocean formed the original fauna of the New Zealand. The arrival of Europeans in the 18th century changed the fauna irreversibly. Rats and stoats became established on the islands and readily took to raiding kakapo burrows to prey on the chicks. The kakapo is consequently now extremely rare and may soon be extinct.

A second New Zealand parrot to exhibit unusual characteristics is the kea. This bird lacks the showy plumage of other parrots, contenting itself with dull brown and drab green feathers. Its upper bill is more sharply curved than that of other birds and is considerably longer than the lower. The kea is a large, powerful and muscular bird which has a diet unusual in parrots. In addition to taking the usual fruits and seeds, it also preys upon insects and avidly takes carrion whenever it is available. Keas have long had an unsavoury reputation as sheep-killers for they have often been seen feasting on sheep carcasses. It is unclear whether the birds are merely scavenging on already dead sheep, or if they attack sick and weak sheep. Stock holders have long shot the kea out of hand and there was once a bounty on these birds, but it is now protected by law.

Such oddities apart, the majority of the parrots can readily be divided into a number of groups. Some of these groupings are taxonomically valid, others are simply an assemblage of birds with a similar appearance or lifestyle.

The macaws are the largest parrots, often stretching more than three feet from the beak to the tip of the long tail feathers. There are 15 species of these extremely colourful birds, all of which are restricted to Central and South America. Sharing much of this range are the 25species of Amazon parrots which are plump green birds only a little smaller than the macaws. Cockatoos are another group of large parrots with a distinct geographical distribution, being restricted to Australasia and the Philippines. They are instantly recognisable by their large erectable crests and are easily tamed, making good pets.

The much smaller parakeets are slim-bodied parrots with long trailing tails. The best known of these is the budgerigar, which has become a popular cage bird and has been selectively bred to produce a wide range of colours in its plumage. In the wild, however, it is green with dark bars and spots. Flying in enormous flocks, the birds move across the arid interior in a constant search for food and water.

Rather more specialised are the lories of Australasia, Southeast Asia and Polynesia. These small birds are brightly coloured and alone account for one third of all parrot species. They have small, weak beaks and gather most of their food by licking pollen and nectar from the interiors of the rich tropical flowers which they frequent. The smallest parrots of all are the aptly named pygmy parrots of which there are only 16 species in New Guinea and neighbouring islands.

Left: The toco toucan of the South American rainforests, the most familiar of the 37 species of toucans. Below: A channel-billed toucan from South America.

Toucans are unusual birds found only in the Amazon Basin and in neighbouring forest lands. They are a brightly coloured group of small to medium-sized birds which are possibly the noisiest birds of South America. They call incessantly throughout the daylight hours with a harsh, grating call which carries surprisingly well through the forest.

The most extraordinary feature of these birds is the huge bill which adorns every species. In some case the bill is as long as the bird's actual body. Though so large the bill is surprisingly light. The outer sheath of coloured horn covers an internal structure of lattice-work bone which imparts size and strength with the minimum of weight.

When feeding the toucan makes great use of this bill. When tackling large fruits, the toucan first slices a chunk off with the serrated edge of its bill then swallows the chunk whole. When eating smaller fruits or berries, the bird plucks the piece of food with the very tip of its bill, tosses its head back and catches the food within its mouth before swallowing. Similar tactics are used when nest-robbing for eggs or chicks.

However, it remains unlikely that the toucan's bill is so amazingly large simply as a food gathering organ. Other birds feed on a similar diet with much smaller beaks. The most probable explanation of the bill is that it is a signalling device of some kind. It may be used in courtship displays or may help to distinguish between different species. Whatever the true purpose of the bill it is clearly successful for the toucans are a thriving group.

1: Green-billed Toucan.
2: Sulphur-crested Cockatoo.
3: Toco Toucan.
4: White-crested Cockatoo.
5: Pink Cockatoo.
6: Ariel Toucan.

CUCKOOS AND TURACOS
Parasitic Nesters

The order Cuculiformes is best known for the cuckoos which account for the vast majority of the species in this group, though the touracos are a familiar part of African fauna. The group is unusual in that although the birds seem physically well adapted to climbing, this is the one thing they cannot do.

Like other birds which climb through trees and scrub, the cuckoos have four toes, with one pair pointing forwards and another backwards. Parrots use this arrangement to great effect when scrambling along branches, but cuckoos are unable to move along branches once they have landed. If they wish to move on they must take to the air and fly to a new perch. By contrast they are agile on the ground with some species being particularly well adapted to running, especially in arid environments.

This apparently curious disability is due to the fact that the internal arrangements of the muscles and tendons of the leg and foot are quite different in the cuckoos than in parrots and others.

The Cuculiformes share a number of features each with another. One of the most noticeable is that they all have a loud, repetitive call. The best known such call is the 'cuckoo' which gave the group its name, but only a few species use this vocalisation.

However, it is the curious and destructive breeding habits of the cuckoos which have made them so well known, none more so than the common cuckoo which is found throughout Europe, Asian forests and much of Africa. This bird is a little over a foot in length and feeds chiefly on insects but will also take earthworms and other invertebrates. In March it moves north from its southern wintering grounds to reach the breeding grounds in more northerly latitudes of Europe and Asia.

Once in the summer lands, the cuckoos begin calling insistently. The familiar 'cuckoo' is the far-carrying cry of the male, while the female has a softer more trembling note. Once mating has taken place the female starts looking for a suitable place to lay her eggs. It is essential that she lays carefully for if she does not the offspring will die. For some days the female will fly over a set territory keeping a watch for other pairs of birds building nests. When the pair lays an egg, the cuckoo is stimulated to lay her own and within a few hours sweeps down on the nest. The cuckoo bears a close similarity to the sparrowhawk and this may frighten the host birds away. Once the egg is laid the female cuckoo flies off in search of more hosts for her total of 5 or 6 eggs.

The cuckoo egg hatches after 12 days, usually before the host eggs hatch. The cuckoo chick has a hollow in its back which is highly sensitive. As it moves around the nest, the other eggs will brush against this spot and stimulate the cuckoo chick to push. It continues to shove until the egg is pushed out of the nest to fall and smash. The other eggs are dealt with in the same way. The chick then opens its mouth and continually demands food from its foster parents. The adult birds rarely, if ever, fail to do so. Their own instinct to feed a chick in the nest is too strong to be refused. Within a few days the chick is actually larger than its host parents, but they feed it until the bird has gained its adult plumage and flies off to care for itself.

The adult cuckoos leave for the wintering grounds in August, but the chicks stay for a further month before flying off and finding their way unaided although they have never made the journey before.

An unusual cuckoo is the roadrunner of the semi-deserts of southern USA and northern Mexico. This bird has abandoned the trees entirely and instead lives on the ground. Its long legs have become adapted to fast running. When disturbed it will dash for the nearest cover at high speed. This acceleration is used in hunting when it will pounce on its prey, including insects, snakes, birds and lizards.

Below: A young cuckoo being fed by a wren, its surrogate parent. The cuckoo dwarfs the wren and has outgrown the nest, but continues to be fed. Bottom: Ross's Touraco from Kenya.

1: Chestnut Cuckoo.
2: Ross's Touraco.
3: Common Cuckoo.
4: Great Blue Touraco.
5: Roadrunner.
6: Helmeted Touraco.

The second family within the Cuculiformes is that encompassing the Turacos of central Africa. These colourful birds are entirely arboreal, reversing the trend of the roadrunners, and are more often heard than seen. They live in the densest forests, hiding in foliage, but have a piercing alarm call which follows humans moving through the forest. They are colourful birds with long tails, erect crests and brilliant hues. The pigments of these birds are unusual for they are water-soluble and fade rapidly in rain. Unlike the cuckoos, the turacos care for their young, building nests high in the trees and feeding them on mashed up fruits.

OWLS
Hunters in the Night

All 140 or so species of owl are grouped together in the order Strigiformes, though they are sometimes divided into two similar families. They are an extremely successful group of birds which has spread out to inhabit every continent except Antarctica. Though they are predatory creatures and have a sharply hooked beak and long clawed toes, the owls are very different from the typical birds of prey.

There are many features which separate owls from other birds of prey, one of which is the foot so apparently similar to that of the eagles and hawks. The owl has four toes each armed with a long, hooked talon. Unlike the birds of prey, however, the owls are able radically to change the configuration of their feet. They can use a standard three-toes forward, one-toe back layout when hunting or can swivel the outer toe backward to give a parrot-like paired toe effect for perching. Such mobility of foot is rare among birds.

More unusual still is the silent flight of the owls. All other birds are rather noisy when flying, producing a series of creaking, whooshing and fluttering sounds. These various noises are produced chiefly by the leading edges of the wings as they cut through the air. As the feathers slice through the air they create turbulence with pockets of still air and fast moving streams interacting with each other to set up vibrations.

The owls, relying as they do on stealth for hunting success, avoid these noises by special adaptations of the leading feathers on the wings. The individual filaments of these lack alternate bards so that they are held together

only loosely. This structure is such that some air can filter through them rather than being cleanly divided as in other birds. This produces a layer of slow-moving air between the stationary pockets and fast-moving streams, thus cutting down on turbulence and noise. A very similar arrangement has recently been adopted by airplane designers to cut down the sound of jets on take off and landing, a feature of great benefit at urban airports.

The owls hunt chiefly at dusk or night and their senses have become attuned to finding prey in poor light conditions. The ears are particularly sensitive being able to pick up the sounds of a scurrying rodent at some distance. The silent flight is important here for loud flapping would interfere with the direction finding ability of the ears. It is suspected that some night-flying owls hunt more by hearing than sight.

Sight is, however, critical in most species. More than most birds of prey, owls have a sense of sight adapted to locating prey with an accuracy which allows a single swoop to stand a high chance of success. The eyes face forward, giving near perfect binary vision. With two eyes focussing on an object at the same time its distance can be gauged accurately. The eyes are surrounded by radiating fans of tiny feathers which may help the bird assess direction in some way. The fact that the eyes face forward means that the owls have a huge blind spot behind them. To get over this the owls are able to twist their heads through a full 180 degrees so as to inspect their surrounding without moving their bodies.

As a rule owls hunt small animals, principally rodents. These are caught and killed before being carried off to a much frequented perch. Here the prey is swallowed whole and the bird remains roosting while the meal is digested. Any bones, fur and other indigestible matter is formed into a compact pellet and vomited out. The rodent hunting activities of owls make them of enormous benefit to farmers in keeping down vermin and they are generally protected.

The barn owl is a particularly widespread species, being found almost throughout the world except on some isolated islands. It is a medium-sized owl at around 13 inches which, like many other owls, nests in hollow trees and lays a clutch of around 5 eggs. The female sits on the eggs and is fed by the male until the young hatch, whereupon both parents hunt. This species has taken to nesting in old buildings, hence its name.

Much larger are the great grey owl and the snowy owl of the more northerly regions of Canada, Europe and Asia, though the great grey is absent from eastern Asia. The snowy owl hunts during the days of the long Arctic summer taking prey larger than that tackled by other owls, including hares and rabbits. It nests on the ground with the male feeding the female while she incubates. The shorteared owl is found in the northern continents, but is also to be seen in South America.

Pell's fishing owl is an oddity for, as its name suggests, it preys chiefly on fish. Its feet and lower legs are unfeathered so that it can plunge its talons into lakes and streams to seize prey without the plumage becoming waterlogged. It is found near water in sub-Saharan Africa.

1: Great Grey Owl.
2: Pell's Fishing Owl.
3: Snowy Owl.
4: Barn Owl.
5: Short-eared Owl.
6: Spotted Owlet.

Left: A magnificent great grey owl resting on a branch while it awaits the onset of dusk before hunting.

SWIFTS AND HUMMINGBIRDS
Expert Fliers

Taken together the swifts and hummingbirds are possibly the most avian of all birds. Their flying abilities are almost legendary, but it is less well recognised that they are poor walkers, indeed some species are virtually helpless on the ground being unable to move at more than the slowest of crawls. The apparently very different families of birds are included within the single order Apodiformes because of various internal features. Perhaps the most important of these is found in the wing structure. The wing bone analogous to the upper arm of humans is noticeably shorter and stronger than in other birds, while the lower wing bones are elongated and form much of the wing. This allows the proportionally much stronger flight muscles a good purchase providing for more efficient use of muscle power.

The swifts are the fastest things on two wings, though quite how fast they fly is a matter of debate. Anyone who has seen the rapid flight of the swift as it chases insects through the skies cannot doubt that they move extremely quickly and the highest officially confirmed speed timed for a swift is 105 miles per hour. Less reliable measurements have recorded birds topping 150 miles per hour and even approaching 200 miles per hour.

One of the more disturbing habits of the common swift is that during the early summer it flies at great speed, screeching its high-pitched call almost continuously. At times the birds will circle house at high speed, a trick which caused rural people to dub it the devil bird and which could frighten anyone not used to the antics.

This immensely high speed is made possible by the long, tapering wings of the swifts which often produce a wingspan much greater than the length of the bird. In flight the birds move with fast, frequent but shallow wingbeats, interrupted by periods of gliding. The wings also act as steering gear for the tails are too frail to turn the bird. Unlike most other birds, the swifts have the ability to beat their wings out of synchronisation with each other, producing twists and spins of amazing agility and speed.

This flying skill is used to catch insects on the wing, but the swifts has sacrificed the ability to walk to enhance their flight and they are helpless on the ground. Many are not even able to take off from the ground but must launch themselves from cliffs or trees. They nest in trees, cliffs and buildings, attaching the nest to the solid base with sticky saliva.

Equally outstanding as fliers are the hummingbirds of the Americas. These birds lack the sheer speed of the swifts, but are outstanding aerobats being able to fly in any direction they desire, even backwards. This amazing ability, shared by no other group of birds, is due to the mobile wings of the bird and an incredibly rapid rate of wingbeat.

The actual size of the wings compared to that of the body is not particularly unusual, but the breastbone of the hummingbird, and the flight muscles attached to it are proportionally larger than in any other bird, accounting for nearly one third of the entire body weight. The short, thick upper wing bone is attached to the body by way of a unique joint which allows it to swivel into many different positions giving the wing a highly manoeuvrable aspect. Using these adaptations the hummingbirds can beat their wings at up to 90 strokes per second to hold themselves aloft. By twisting the wings the birds can subtly alter the direction of thrust and so move themselves minutely through the air. The high speed of the wings sets up a distinct buzzing sound which has given this group their common name.

The purpose of this aerobatic ability is to enable the hummingbirds to feed on the nectar of the many tropical flowers found in their range. The birds hover in front of the flowers and probe the depths with their bills in order to suck up the sugar rich nectar. The enormous amount of energy in the nectar is swiftly converted to body energy to maintain flight. The hummingbirds also eat some insects which they find in the flowers or hunt on the wing. The many differently shaped bills are probably adaptations to feeding on different types of flower. The swordbilled hummingbird has a bill longer than the rest of its body and feeds on long, tubular shaped flowers.

In addition to their spectacular flight, hummingbirds are noted for their brilliant plumage. The males are particularly vivid being adorned with hues of green, red, orange, black, blue and almost any other shade imaginable. As if to make themselves even more attractive the birds sport a striking and impressive variety of crests, tufts and trailing tail feathers.

1: *Swift.*
2: *Crimson Topaz Hummingbird.*
3: *Frilled Coquette Hummingbird.*
4: *Sword-billed Hummingbird.*
5: *Popelaire's Thornbill Hummingbird.*
6: *Ruby-throated Hummingbird.*

Below: A broad-tailed hummingbird manoeuvres for position before sucking nectar from a bloom.

TROGONS
Tropical Beauties

The beautiful trogons are widely spread through the tropical regions of the world and are placed in an order all their own. This individuality is largely due to their feet which, like those of parrots, have one pair of toes facing forwards and the other pair facing backwards. Unlike parrots, however, the trogons have the first two toes to the rear and the second pair turned forward. No other birds have such an arrangement and this was enough for naturalists to place the trogons in a group apart.

Most of these birds are about a foot in length, though the long and spectacular tail feathers can easily double this measurement, or even treble it. They live in the dense tropical forests of Africa, India and Central and South America where they are very rarely seen by man, despite their bright and showy plumage. The trogons escape notice because of, rather than despite, their plumage. When perched in the trees, the greens, reds and blues of their coloration matches the heavy foliage and tropical blooms which surround them. The contrasting patches of colour serve to break up the outline of these birds so that not even their silhouette gives them away.

The trogons have adopted a distinctive method of finding food which is ideally suited to their habitat. Sitting on their perches, the trogons remain motionless so as to blend into the background. Their eyes, meanwhile are constantly searching for a passing insect as it moves through the hot, humid air. As soon as a likely victim comes close to the waiting bird, it leaps from its perch and drives forward with swift, powerful beats of its wings. Once the insect is caught, the bird retreats to its perch to devour its meal.

The Asian species of trogon feed exclusively on insects, but the American species consume large quantities of fruit as well. Their technique for collecting fruit is very much like that for catching insects. From their perches, the birds dash to a fruit bush or tree, grab a mouthful and return to their perch to eat it. The flight is repeated time after time.

Trogons have short, blunt wings which are ideal for fast take off and the type of powerful strokes needed to surprise a flying insect. They are, however, ill-suited to sustained flight and the birds rarely attempt to fly more than a few yards at a time.

All species nest in holes, though the different species vary greatly in exactly how they go about the process. The Asian and African species tend to utilise natural hollows and cracks in tree trunks or in fallen timber, but the American trogons will often dig their own nesting holes out of rotting stumps or dead trees. Both parents help in the task which may take over two weeks to complete. The garter trogon of Venezuela has been observed making nests in large wasps' nests whose inhabitants had first been devoured.

Depending on species, two, three or four eggs may be laid, rarely more. They are pale and rounded and are cared for by both parents. Once the young are hatched both parents hunt for food and take their turns guarding the nest. The males, with their magnificent long tail plumes, suffer during the breeding season. The constant work of excavating the nest and of clambering in and out of it tears at the plumage. By the time the young leave the nest, the tail feathers of the father are badly battered, and sometimes broken off completely.

The species with the longest tail of all is the famous quetzal of Central America. This truly magnificent bird has green head and body plumage with a red breast, a bluish tinge to the back and enormously long tail plumes which can be anything up to two feet in length.

Over the years many legends have attached themselves to this bird. The Aztecs, who established an empire covering much of Mexico in the 15th and 16th centuries, considered it to be a holy bird, the favourite of the sky god Quetzalcoatlus. The long tail plumes were avidly collected and used by priests in the ceremonial life of the nation which involved the sacrifice of hundreds of humans at a time. The Aztecs, however, were anxious not to harm the bird. Once the tail feathers were plucked, the birds were released.

In more recent years the belief grew up that if the bird was captured it would die of a broken heart. This supposed love of liberty led to the bird being adopted as the national bird of Guatemala, giving its name to the inland city of Quetzaltenango.

1: Scarlet-rumped Trogon.
2: Quetzal.
3: Collared Trogon.
4: Cuban Trogon.
5: White-tailed Trogon.

Far left: A violaceous trogon of Costa Rica. Left: The quetzal bird, the most magnificent of all the trogons.

KINGFISHERS
Darting Jewels

The 86 species of kingfisher can be divided neatly into two groups; those which fish and those which do not. There are several differences between the two groups, most of which are concerned with their hunting patterns, but they share much in common as well.

All kingfishers have long, dagger-like bills mounted on heads rather large for the body size. Most are brightly coloured, some almost dazzling in their beauty. They are all rather stocky birds with broad bodies and tails which are short and wide in most species. Their wings are short and stumpy but they are able to fly fast and straight for short distances. The kingfishers are placed within the order Coraciiformes, which also covers the hornbills and bee-eaters. This is largely due to the internal construction of their leg muscles and palate. Almost the only external identifying feature of the group is that their toes are joined along part of their length. Even this characteristic is almost absent in some species.

Of the fishing kingfishers probably the most typical and certainly the most familiar is the common kingfisher which ranges widely across Europe, southern Asia and central Africa. One of the most instantly recognisable birds in Europe, the kingfisher is a small bird barely 6 inches long but it is brilliantly coloured with a chestnut chest, white throat and iridescent blue-green back and head. Chestnut and white cheek patches complete the flamboyant plumage of this bird. The bright flashy feathers make the kingfisher conspicuous, as is its intention. Birds of prey tend to avoid the kingfisher for it has an unpleasant flavour. The bright plumage helps the predators recognise the bird and so avoid it.

True to its name the kingfisher is expert at catching fish, principally small minnows which it can swallow whole. When hunting, the bird will sit on a branch or post over freshwater, usually a small stream or river but occasionally a lake or pond. Remaining absolutely motionless, the bird sits upright, its head bent down to watch the waters below. When a fish swims within range, the bird launches itself into the air in a flurry of brilliant plumage and plunges down to dive into the water, seizing the prey.

Unlike most fish-eating birds, kingfishers cannot swim. Instead they lift off from rest, carrying their prey back to the perch. There the kingfisher juggles the catch until it is head down before swallowing it whole.

During cold winters, when fresh water is liable to freeze, the kingfishers may move to estuaries or even the seashore in search of food. During particularly cold snaps many birds die of starvation. In the bitter winter of 1962 to 1963 in Britain one river lost 90% of its kingfishers.

The ancient Greeks knew the kingfisher as the halcyon and believed it to be a favourite of the gods. They also held that kingfishers built floating nests far out to sea. It was said that during the breeding fortnight the gods held the elements in check to provide the kingfishers with days of calm and sunlight. The Greeks called these the halcyon days, a phrase which has remained with us.

In fact kingfishers nest in burrows in the banks of the rivers which they fish. Both parents help dig the narrow tunnel which after three feet opens out into a nesting chamber. The only lining given to the nest is that of discarded fish bones. On these are laid six or seven white eggs which hatch after three weeks. A little over three weeks later the hatchlings can fly and are taught the skills of fishing by their parents. When the young can care for themselves, the parents abandon them and raise a second brood before autumn closes in.

The non-fishing or forest kingfishers are typified by the kookaburra of Australia, which is best known for its call which resembles demonic laughter to such an extent that it has frightened many who hear it for the first time. The kookaburra is a large bird, about the size of a crow, which lives in open woodland and grassland. Like other forest kingfishers it has a heavy bill rather broader and flatter than its fishing cousins.

It uses this bill to prey upon a wide variety of animals, from insects and slugs to reptiles and chicks of other birds. Particularly idiosyncratic is the kookaburra's technique for hunting snakes. Pouncing on the intended prey, the kookaburra seizes it by the neck, thus rendering the deadly fangs useless. The snake is then lifted high in the air, and released to fall to its death. The kookaburra, like other forest kingfishers, is respected by farmers for it keeps down a large number of pests.

1: *Blue-winged Kookaburra.*
2: *White-headed Kingfisher.*
3: *Rufous-billed Kookaburra.*
4: *Amazon Kingfisher.*
5: *White-throated Kingfisher.*
6: *Chestnut-collared Kingfisher.*
7: *Yellow-billed Kingfisher.*
8: *European Kingfisher.*
9: *Forest Kingfisher.*

Left: A European kingfisher with a small fish clasped in its bill. Below: The Australian kookaburra, the largest and loudest of the kingfishers.

BEE-EATERS, ROLLERS AND HOOPOE
Aerial Acrobats

True to their name the bee-eaters consume large numbers of bees and wasps throughout their range, which is restricted to warmer areas of the Old World, principally Africa. The birds are relatives of the kingfishers, being members of the order Coraciiformes. Like other members of that group, the bee-eaters have toes which are joined along part of their length and have a plumage which can be highly colourful.

Bee-eaters are distinguished from other members of the order by their sleek bodies, long pointed wings and weak legs. The bee-eaters also have bills which carry a ridge along the top and are often slightly curved. More distinctive still are the tails which tend to feature a pair of central feathers which are much longer than the other tail feathers.

The basic diet of all bee-eaters is the various insects of the bee and wasp families, though the birds are likely to prey upon large insects of almost any description. In temperate parts of their range, particularly Europe, the bee-eaters are regarded as something of a pest. They consume vast numbers of bees and have thus earned the enmity of apiarists who rely on their bees for their honey.

The European bee-eater which causes this damage is one of the more brightly coloured members of its family having a blue chest, green and yellow body and a brown cape covering the shoulders and top of the head. When hunting it will sit motionless on a post or branch, waiting for an insect to come within range. Then it powers out with rapid, strong wingbeats, to seize the victim in

mid-air. Turning sharply the bird returns to its perch where it strokes the prey against the wood before devouring it. It is thought that this habit might serve the purpose of removing the sting.

The European bee-eater migrates south for the winter, following the warmth to find the abundance of insects it needs to survive. In the tropical regions the birds join the majority of bee-eater species, such as the carmine bee-eater of central Africa, the red-throated bee-eater of East Africa and the blue-throated bee-eater.

In these more southerly climates the bee-eaters are regarded, not as a pest, but as a positive blessing. The tropical species feast upon not only bees but also locusts, which they consume in large numbers when the insects swarm, so rendering great service to farmers. The southern species also differ from their northern cousins in being more active fliers. They fly in search of insects, often diving and swooping high in the air as they pursue their prey.

More remarkable still are the flying antics of the rollers, which gave the birds of this group their name. At any time of the year rollers can be observed swooping and twisting in the air in search of insects, but it is during courtship that they show their abilities to the full. The aerobatics in which the birds indulge have become almost legendary. Climbing high into the sky, the birds will plummet downwards at tremendous speed, then curve upward, using their momentum to lift them high though their wings are folded. Twists, turns, rolls and somersaults all form part of the remarkable courtship flight.

Like other members of the order Coraciiformes, rollers are essentially burrow-nesters. Some species dig nests in termite mounds while others take over hollows in trees vacated by woodpeckers in preference to burrows in the ground. They produce rather fewer eggs than is the norm, rarely laying more than four in a clutch.

Perhaps the most unusual bird in the Coraciiformes order is the hoopoe which is sufficiently different from other birds in the order to be given a family all its own. This striking bird is instantly recognisable throughout its range which spreads from central Europe, through southern Asia and into central Africa. Its reddish-brown body is just under a foot in length and is adorned with boldly striped black and white wings and tail. The head is topped by a large erect crest of reddish feathers with black tips.

The hoopoe is essentially a ground bird which pushes its long, curved bill into soft earth or rotting vegetation in search of worms, insects and other invertebrates. It will take to the wing to hunt flying insects, though its flight is rather slow and uneven.

The most notorious fact about the hoopoe is its filthy nest. The bird lays its eggs in hollow trees, or in openings in buildings, where it incubates for 17 days and feeds the nestlings for a further 25. Throughout this period the birds never clean the nest to remove either excrement or putrefying food scraps. The resultant smell is made worse by the powerful musty odour which the female develops during the breeding season. Some experts have suggested that these characteristics are a protection against nest-raiders in much the same way as the skunk's repulsive scent glands deter predators.

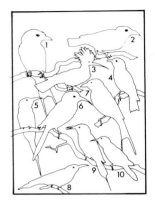

1: *Lilac-breasted Roller.*
2: *Indian Roller.*
3: *Hoopoe.*
4: *European Roller.*
5: *Carmine Bee-eater.*
6: *Red-bearded Bee-eater.*
7: *Blue-bellied Roller.*
8: *European Bee-eater.*
9: *Blue-throated Bee-eater.*
10: *Red-throated Bee-eater.*

Left: The Carmine Bee-eater of Malawi which does great service to local humans by eating crop-destroying locusts.

HORNBILLS
Birds in Prison

Their joined toes mark the 44 species of hornbill as members of the order Coraciiformes alongside the kingfishers and rollers, but apart from this feature they are very distinctive birds. Fossil evidence shows the hornbills to have been a separate family as long ago as 50 million years and their origins probably stretch back a further 15 million years to the time of the dinosaurs.

The most noticeable feature of the hornbills which marks them off from the other Coraciiformes is their sheer size. The great Indian hornbill is over 5 feet in length and most other species are only slightly smaller. Even the smallest hornbill is over 18 inches in length, the size of the largest kingfisher and larger than any roller or bee-eater.

The second distinctive feature of the hornbills is that which gave the family its common name, the huge bill. Like other Coraciiformes, hornbills have large heads, but these seem diminutive compared to the bills, some of which carry outgrowths or casques. Though large the bills are not heavy for they are made up of bone-like material which is arranged in a honeycomb-like structure which gives strength without weight. The only exception is the casque of the helmeted hornbill from Malaya which is made up of solid ivory. The locals have long used the ivory to make talismans but international demand for their craftwork has led to a recent fall in the populations of this striking bird.

Hornbills use their extraordinary, down-curved bills to gather a wide variety of food, though most species tend to specialise in one diet or another. Several species rely heavily on fruit for sustenance. These birds tend to frequent the upper branches of tropical forests where they can find sufficient quantities of ripe fruit to satisfy their appetites. Other hornbills, usually those found in open woodland or savannah, rely more on insects for sustenance. All hornbills have a liking for small reptiles and mammals and take them whenever possible. Like the toucans, which also have large bills, the hornbills often manipulate the food with the tips of their beaks before tossing it up in the air and catching it in their mouths preparatory to swallowing.

Some species have the peculiar habit of making towards the smell of fire, while most other animals flee from flames. The reason is that grass fires disturb the resident insects, sending them scurrying from cover. The hornbills keep a short distance in front of the advancing flames and feast upon the insects more intent upon avoiding the fire than on keeping an eye open for predators.

Even more curious is the nesting habit which is common to all hornbills, although details differ between species. Hornbills appear to pair for life, certainly the bond between the pair needs to be very strong considering the ordeal the birds go through. The eggs are laid in the hollow of a tree which may be natural or which has been enlarged by the hornbills. Usually between one and six eggs are laid on which the female sits.

The male then brings mud and other materials to the female and together they block the entrance to the nest until only a thin slit, just wide enough to admit the male's beak is left. The mud mixture gradually dries to a rock-hard consistency which is proof against the attacks of even the most determined nest-robber. Any creature which begins to make progress against the barrier is immediately assaulted by the female and driven off.

The male gathers food from the surrounding countryside and brings it to the nest, passing it to the female trough the slit. As soon as she is imprisoned the female moults, losing her tail, wing and body feathers in rotation. When the young hatch, the female remains in the nest for several days, taking food from the male and passing it on to the chicks. When the young have grown large enough to be left alone, the female breaks out, often with the aid of the male, to help in the task of feeding the young. In several species, the young then rebuild the protective barrier. At this point the female is virtually unable to fly and must spend sometime stretching her cramped wing muscles before taking to the air.

The two parents then feed the young through the slit in the mud wall until they have developed their adult plumage. The wall is then broken down for the final time and the young emerge. Though perfectly formed, they are unable to fly for several days. They spend this time flapping about until they learn how to fend for themselves.

Hornbills are extremely loud birds both in their habits and their voices. They call loudly, and usually harshly, around dawn and dusk uttering either loud booms, grating chatters or piercing screams according to species. Because their flight feathers are particularly hard and unyielding, the wings set up a great amount of turbulence as they cut through the air. This creates a loud flapping noise which announces the presence of a hornbill making its way through the sky.

1: Grey Hornbill.
2: Yellow-casqued Hornbill.
3: Trumpeter Hornbill.
4: Blyth's Wreathed Hornbill.
5: Great Indian Hornbill.
6: Yellow-billed Hornbill.
7: Ground Hornbill (2).

Far left: The remarkable nest of a yellow-billed hornbill which has been opened up to reveal the sealed-in fledglings. The open gap is usually closed by a sheet of glass through which cameras monitor the progress of the hatchlings. Left: Ground Hornbills in Kenya.

WOODPECKERS
Avian Carpenters

By far the largest family of birds within the order Piciformes with around 209 species, the woodpeckers are also the most specialised. They are adapted to a single way of life by a number of physical features which make a woodpecker instantly recognisable as being just that and nothing else.

The lifestyle to which woodpeckers have become specialised is that of arboreal insect hunter, though some species feed on the ground as well as in trees. Woodpeckers have strongly clawed feet which, as in all Piciformes, have a pair of toes facing forwards and another backwards. This is an ideal arrangement for gripping the rough bark of the trees on which they feed. The legs are short so that the body is held close to the trunk. Aiding the legs in keeping the bird fixed to the tree is the tail which is made up of a number of extremely strong, stiff feathers. By pushing this against the trunk, the bird can

brace itself securely to withstand the forces set up by its battering the trunk with its bill. So effective is the triple arrangement of legs and tail that woodpeckers can cling not only to vertical trunks but to the under sides of branches as well.

The birds feed on the grubs of insects which live in burrows beneath the bark of trees, feeding on wood or on sap. As the woodpecker moves across the bark it searches for crannies and holes which might betray the opening to such a burrow. Having found a likely spot, the bird hammers away at the trunk in an attempt to break into the insect's home.

Woodpeckers use their strong, tough beaks to break through the bark. Shaped like chisels, the bills are long, straight and sharp and are mounted on skull bones which are much thicker and stronger than in other birds as an adaptation to absorb repeated impacts. The head can be moved back and forth with great speed and strength by the neck and shoulder muscles of the bird.

Once through to a cavity beneath the bark, the woodpecker flicks out a tongue which is every bit as specialised as the beak. The root of the tongue is curled round inside the skull, reaching from the base of the mouth, round the back of the brain and eventually being secured on bones near the nostrils. This enables the bird to shoot out its tongue to a great length, reaching many inches beyond the tip of its beak. The end of the tongue is equipped with a number of backward-pointing bristles. The bristles are used to ensnare the insect larvae found in the tunnels beneath the bark, and hold the victims firm while the woodpecker withdraws the tongue. Some species of woodpecker have a sticky saliva with which the tongue is coated before it is inserted.

When undisturbed a woodpecker will tend to follow a set feeding pattern. Fluttering through the forest it comes to rest at the base of a tree. It then begins to climb up the trunk, moving around the tree as it rises so as to cover every area of bark. When a large branch is encountered, the bird moves out along the limb before returning to the main trunk and continuing upward. When the bird has reached as far as it can go, it flies off to land at the base of another tree and begins the process again. When a human or other intruder arrives, however, the woodpecker alters its standard spiral pattern so as to remain on the opposite side of the tree from the interloper.

The nests of wild bees and wasps are a boon to woodpeckers which bore quickly through the fragile nest walls to find the larvae which are eaten in quantity. This habit of attack has been adapted for use against domestic beehives and many apiarists treat woodpeckers as a pest which will bore through the shell of a hive to destroy a whole generation of worker bees.

Those species which feed on the ground have retained the typical woodpeckers' feeding technique of probing beneath stones and logs with the long tongue. Ants form the bulk of the diet of most ground species though other insects and their grubs are also taken.

The vast majority of woodpeckers use their bills not only to feed but also to construct their nests. Selecting a section of rotten wood a pair hammer away with their bills to excavate a hole several inches deep before turning vertically downward in order to hollow out a shaft which ends in a slightly flared chamber. This is lined with nothing except wood chips before the white eggs, numbering anything from three to eight, are laid. The chicks are fed by both parents with insects and larvae until they are old enough to care for themselves, which may be as many as thirty days after hatching.

Closely related to the woodpeckers, and usually placed in the same family, are the wrynecks and piculets. The wrynecks are found in Africa, Europe and parts of Asia. These primitive birds lack the boring beak of the woodpeckers and rely on their long tongue to scoop up ants and other insects. Piculets are much smaller than either woodpeckers or wrynecks, rarely being over 4 inches in length. They catch insects with their tongues and although they cannot excavate wood are more arboreal than the wrynecks.

1: Green Woodpecker.
2: Golden-backed Woodpecker.
3: Black Woodpecker.
4: Grey-headed Woodpecker.
5: Greater Spotted Woodpecker.
6: Three-toed Woodpecker.
7: Crimson-backed Woodpecker.
8: Red-headed Woodpecker.

Left: A female greater spotted woodpecker which can be distinguished from the male by the lack of a red patch on the back of the neck. This is the most common woodpecker in European woodlands but is also found in North Africa and parts of Asia.

SONGBIRDS
The Most Successful Birds

Known by a variety of common names, such as songbirds and perching birds, the scientific order Passeriformes is without doubt the most outstandingly successful group of birds in the world today. Of the approximately 9,000 species of bird in existence no fewer than 5,100 are songbirds. This amazing dominance is due to the ability of the group to adapt to a wide range of habitats and foods, producing a vast number of species adapted to different styles of life. All species are, nonetheless, land birds having no liking for water.

The classification of the group is one of the most contentious and controversial areas of ornithology. There are almost as many methods of classifying the songbirds as there are ornithologists for the very diversity of the species makes them difficult to fit into a cohesive pattern. Some families are as distinct from each other as are some orders of birds while others are so similar that many scientists refuse to accept them as families at all. Even when the individuality of families is established it is unclear exactly how they are related to each other. Various authorities group the families in many ways, depending on which feature they consider to be the dominant for classification purposes.

Though they are such a diverse group of birds, the Passeriformes share several features in common which keep them firmly in a single order. All species have well-developed voice boxes which enable the group to produce a bewildering array of songs and calls and which accounts for the common name of songbirds. Some scientists subdivide the group into sub-orders according to the structure of the voice box. This produces four sub-orders each with a different number of paired muscles operating the song-producing chamber. The most advanced birds in this pattern have eight pairs of muscles and can produce the greatest range of song. This ability is most marked in the males which often sing as part of the courtship ritual or in order to mark their territory.

The common name of perching birds alludes to the structure of the feet which is unique to the Passeriformes. The foot consists of four toes, each springing from an 'ankle' at the end of the leg. These toes are unwebbed and are able to grasp with great strength. The hind toe is usually rather longer and stronger than the others and is opposable. It is the hind toe wrapping around a twig or branch in the opposite direction to the other three which gives the Passeriformes their superb ability to perch on a variety of locations.

A few other physical features mark the songbirds out from all other orders, but most of these are internal and are not immediately obvious. One of the more important of these is the unique arrangement of bones in the palate which is shared by all species in the group.

Behaviourally the songbirds show a remarkable variation which has much to do with the range of habitats in which they live and the foods which they eat. They do, however, share a broadly similar breeding pattern. The songbirds are amongst the best nest-builders in the avian world. Most species create fairly complex structures comparing favourably with other birds the nests of which may by fairly scrappy or entirely non-existent. Some species build enormous nests which are highly impressive as examples of animal architecture. Some even appear to design their structures with as much regard to aesthetic considerations as to comfort or security.

Within this nest the birds lay a number of eggs which vary greatly in size, shape and colour depending on varying needs of camouflage and practicality. When the young hatch they are blind and almost invariably naked. After a few days a covering of soft down appears to be replaced by true feathers as the chick grows and its eyes open. The young are most often fed by the parents on insects, regardless of the adult diet, so a good supply of insects is essential to a breeding population. This does not halt the birds from migrating to other habitats during the non-breeding season, but it does rather limit the ranges of the nesting grounds.

Using the arrangement of muscles within the voicebox as a determining factor ornithologists divide the songbirds into two groups; the primitive, or suboscine, and the advanced, or oscine. Within the suboscine are included three sub-orders with four or less pairs of muscles. The oscines have five or more.

Below: A male pied flycatcher resting on a branch after catching a beakful of its insect food.

The most diverse and successful family of the suboscine songbirds is the tyrannidae, more popularly known as tyrant flycatchers. Some 370 species of bird are included in this group, though some may be only sub-species. They are spread throughout the two Americas from Cape Horn to the Arctic Ocean, though most species are restricted to tropical forests. The birds are known under a variety of common names, including kiskadee, kingbird and phoebe as well as flycatcher.

As their name suggests, the flycatchers are active insect hunters. They catch their prey on the wing, being agile and swift fliers well able to outpace the majority of insects. Some species hunt by perching on a post or branch and waiting for a victim to come close. Then the bird lunges forward, flying with swift sure wingbeats which allow it to snap up the prey before it is aware it is under attack. Other species prefer to race through the forests, catching their quarry in high-speed chase.

Flycatchers are neither shy nor retiring and often hunt in open glades where they can easily be seen. They also have loud and insistent songs which are repeated for hours on end. The wood peewee is a particularly repetitive caller, crying its high-pitched call from dawn till dusk. Some species appear to be immune to bee

1: *Buff-breasted Flycatcher.*
2: *Least Flycatcher.*
3: *Great-crested Flycatcher.*
4: *Black Phoebe.*
5: *Eastern Wood Pewee.*
6: *Vermilion Flycatcher.*
7: *Thick-billed Kingbird.*
8: *Great Kiskadee.*
9: *Fork-tailed Flycatcher.*
10: *Superb Lyrebird.*
11: *Scissor-tailed Flycatcher.*
12: *Eastern Kingbird.*

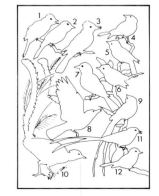

stings, or at least ignore them, and can cause enormous damage to honey harvests by invading hives and consuming large numbers of bees. More constructively, the birds habitually build their own nests close to those of wasps whenever possible.

One of the most impressive of the primitive songbirds is the lyrebird, of which there are only two species both of which are found in southern Australia. These birds are large for songbirds, being up to 2 feet (60 cm) in length, and have several other features which make them distinct from other songbirds. They live in dense cover in the forests preying upon insects which they find by tearing apart rotten wood or stirring up leaves with their powerful legs.

It is the tail which makes these birds so distinctive. The tail feathers are unusually long and strongly resemble a lyre in shape. The two outer feathers curve out as they rise, turning in again near the centre before turning sharply out again before the top. Rising vertically between the 'frame' of the lyre are a number of white quills which form the 'strings' of the instrument. Though usually depicted in classic lyre shaped configuration, the feathers are actually waved around during the courtship dance and may assume a variety of patterns.

The nomenclature of the higher songbirds is among the most difficult in science, and the warblers do little to clarify the confusion. The birds which are known a warblers belong to a very different family from the warblers of America. The New World warblers, sometimes called wood-warblers, are placed in the family parulidae and are often closely linked to the vireos, which they resemble.

These warblers are generally small, brightly coloured birds though the plumage often becomes duller towards the end of the summer. Of the 120 species all are restricted to the Americas, though they are to be found in a wide range of areas and habitats. Many species are strongly migratory between tropical and temperate America. In the spring the bright warblers fly north from Central America to seek nesting grounds in the forests of Canada and the northern United States. As the birds arrive in spring they are very vociferous, filling the woods with their light, trilling songs. Later in the season the

birds lose their song and adopt a dull brown-grey plumage before returning south. Other species are non-migratory, remaining in the warmer climates year-round. Some of the tropical species feed on nectar, spurning the insect diet of the majority of species.

Wood-warblers build small half-globe nests in trees and bushes, often a considerable height above the ground. In some species the male plays a large part in caring for the young. He may help build the nest and feed the female while she incubates. More normally he has little to do with nesting, a task reserved for the female.

Below: A yellow-rumped warbler feeding insects to its young in Wyoming. Below left: A yellow warbler from the Galapagos Islands.

The vireos are similar in appearance to wood-warblers and share with them certain anatomical features which encourages many scientists to place the two families close together. Like the wood-warblers, vireos are rather small birds which are restricted to the New World and which migrate between northern breeding grounds and the tropical belt.

One of the commonest and most easily recognised vireos is the red-eyed vireo which may be seen as far north as Canada and as far south as Argentina. The lack of barred marking on the wing combined with a grey cap and bold white stripe reaching back from the beak make the bird unmistakable. The vivid red eye which gave the species its name is only visible at close quarters. The bird prefers to live in deciduous woodland in which there is plenty of dense undergrowth and leaf litter where it can hunt out berries and insects. During these forays, the red-eyed vireo chatters and calls almost incessantly, a habit which caused the first Europeans to encounter the bird to dub it the preacher-bird.

The remaining 41 species in the vireo family consist of 36 true vireos, 2 peppershrikes and 3 shrikevireos. The peppershrikes are almost as persistent in their singing as the red-eyed vireo. Though rarely seen, the birds are often heard singing in the forests of Central and South America where they have their homes. The shrike-vireos are more like the true vireos than the heavy peppershrikes but tend to be more colourful. They inhabit the highest branches of tropical forests and are rarely seen and little studied.

One of the smaller, but well-known, families of songbirds is the mimidae, better known as the mocking-

1: Yellow Warbler.
2: Yellow-breasted Chat.
3: Northern Parula.
4: Black-throated Blue Warbler.
5: American Redstart.
6: Black-throated Grey Warbler.
7: Slate-throated Redstart.
8: Chestnut-sided Shrike Vireo.
9: Prothonotary Warbler.
10: Yellow-throated Vireo.
11: Red-eyed Vireo.

birds. Restricted to the New World, the mockingbirds are generally rather small birds, with few species being more than 12 inches (30 cm) in length. One of the most brilliantly coloured species is the Mexican blue mockingbird which has a rich blue plumage, broken by a black flash across the eye. These birds are fiercely territorial and protect their little realm against not only other mockingbirds but also intruding mammals and reptiles.

The 9 species of true mockingbirds have become famous for their incredible singing abilities. Mockingbirds will sing at any time of the day or night, usually choosing an isolated tree stump or fence post on which to perform to best advantage. The actual song of the mockingbird is pleasant enough, but it is the mimicking skills which have made these birds famous. In the course of a single singing performance a mockingbird may reproduce the songs of over 30 different birds, all with an exactness and skill which is quite extraordinary. The birds will even pick up and reproduce sounds which have nothing to do with birds at all. More than one resident of the southern United States has been puzzled by a repeatedly ringing telephone or doorbell, only to find that a mockingbird has been producing the sounds.

Included within the same family as the mockingbirds are the catbirds and thrashers, which are likewise restricted to the New World. Catbirds tend to remain in dense wooded cover where they search for berries or fruits. Sometimes catbirds take up residence close to a house and can become rather friendly. The calls produced by the catbirds do include some attempts at imitations, but are largely restricted to soft mewing sounds. The thrashers are found in open woodland from California to the West Indies and are even more disinclined to mimic than are the catbirds.

Usually placed close to the mockingbirds in any taxonomic breakdown of the songbirds are the thrushes, though the exact relationship is still a matter of debate. The links between thrushes and other groups of songbirds is equally controversial. Until recently it was common practice to place the thrushes in the family turdidae with such birds as babblers, parrotbills, flycatchers and Old

World warblers in separate families. It was common practice, however, to acknowledge that the various families were closely related. In more recent times it has become more acceptable to place all these birds together in one family, the muscicapidae, with what were previously families relegated to sub-family rank. Whether such an arrangement reflects the true taxonomic relationship between these birds is not certain, though there is undoubtedly a very close link of some kind.

Taking the muscicapidae as a valid family, it is the largest of all having over 1,000 species included within it. Within this huge group the thrushes are one of the largest sub-families managing to muster 306 species. Many of these are particularly common and well-known birds throughout their range.

The bird which has given its name to the family, the song thrush, is typical in being a familiar and much loved bird throughout its range which stretches across most of Europe and deep into western Asia. This small brown bird has a distinctive white breast decorated with reddish-brown speckles. Other thrushes share this coloration, but only the songthrush has a clear, penetrating call which it repeats twice over. The song thrush preys upon worms and snails, which it devours eagerly and in large numbers. To deal with snails, the bird chooses a favourite stone against which it beats the snail until the shell breaks and the soft body within can be reached.

Even more familiar in Europe, and present as far east as China, is the blackbird. This opportunistic bird has successfully taken advantage of human environments. It has adapted its woodland habits to suit the gardens of suburbia with great success. It finds lawns and flower borders ideal places to search out the earthworms and insects on which it lives. The movement into gardens began around 1850 and has continued until the blackbird

Left: The mockingbird which can imitate a wide range of sounds. Above: A European Robin. The male uses its red breast as a threat display when challenging other males for territory.

1: Stonechat.
2: Mexican Blue Mockingbird.
3: Nightingale.
4: Eastern Bluebird.
5: Songthrush.
6: European Robin.
7: Orange-billed Nightingale Thrush.
8: European Redstart.
9: Blackbird.
10: American Robin.
11: European Wheatear.

Top: Goldcrest with chicks.
Bottom: A female blackcap on
her nest.

is one of the most prolific birds in its range. Its beautiful, soft whistling call dominates the dawn chorus in many areas, though it may be heard at any time of day.

An equally persistent singer is the European robin which lives throughout Europe and parts of western Europe. The male robin sings to defend its territory, puffing out its red breast as a visual display while the warbling call carries through the air. Territorial disputes are particularly frequent and noisy during the autumn when that summer's chicks are attempting to establish their own territories before the winter closes down. Towards the end of winter, mating songs replace territorial calls ensuring that the robin is a vociferous songbird year-round.

The American robin boasts the striking red breast only in the male, and is actually more closely related to the song thrush than to the European robin. They are more likely to abandon northern lands during the winter to take more in the way of berries and fruits than its European counterpart.

Also noted for its red breast is the stonechat of Europe and Africa, while the European wheatear sports a pale lemon breast. Many other species of thrush are notable for having breasts of a more distinctive colour than the rest of their bodies, which tend towards the dull and drab.

Common terminology has made the classification of the songbirds far from easy, and this is particularly true when dealing with unrelated but superficially similar bird families in widely separated areas. When Europeans first arrived in the New World, for example, they were confronted by birds which were outwardly very similar to the warblers and flycatchers with which they were familiar at home. Not unnaturally the settlers dubbed these new species warblers and flycatchers. When it was discovered that the birds were unrelated the common names had already gained widespread usage and it proved impossible to alter them.

It is for this reason that New World warblers belong to the family parulidae while the Old World warblers are classified as sylvinae, a sub-family of the muscicapidae or thrush family. The latter are typically rather small birds usually marked by drab browns and greys which make them difficult to spot in woodland. The blackcap is an exception having a noticeable black patch on top of its head. Though inconspicuous, the warblers number nearly 400 species spread across Europe, Asia, and Africa. A handful of species have invaded the New World, confusing the demarcation between these birds and the New World warblers even further. More confusing still are the few species of brightly coloured birds which are commonly termed wrens, though they do not belong to the wren family.

The vast majority of Old World warblers are woodland birds, though a few have taken to more open land such as meadows and marshes. They are highly active birds, flying and hopping through the trees and undergrowth with a swift, jerky action. The majority of species feed on insects, some to the exclusion of all other food, a fact which assures them of the affections of farmers and gardeners. A few, however, spoil their reputation by taking berries and fruits.

Warblers are found spread from the Arctic tundra south to the hot scrub forests of Africa. They are however an essentially warmth-loving group. When the cold winter weather closes in they abandon most of the northern parts of their range to migrate further south.

The Old World flycatchers are similarly unrelated to the New World flycatchers, belonging instead to the sub-family muscicapinae the nominate sub-family of the family muscicapidae. As their name suggests these birds are exclusively insect-eaters. The beak of most species is wide and flat, to form an efficient insect trap, and is surrounded by stout bristles which may act as triggers, giving a final tactile signal to the bird that the prey had entered the mouth. As with many other insect hunting birds, the flycatchers spend large periods of time resting on post or isolated branches. When an insect comes within range, the bird flies out to snap it up.

The flycatchers share much of their range with the warblers, but tend to be more numerous and diverse in Australia and Africa. It is to these warm lands that many species found in temperate regions migrate for the winter. A great many species tend towards growing colourful plumage with blues, red and yellows dominating, especially in the males. By contrast their songs are rather underdeveloped. A few species are capable of producing melodious calls, but most are restricted to short, repetitive notes which may sound rather grating. Flycatchers

1: Reed Warbler.
2: Willow Warbler.
3: Paradise Flycatcher.
4: Spotted Flycatcher.
5: Goldcrest.
6: Dunnock.
7: Superb Blue Wren.
8: Blackcap.
9: Narcissus Flycatcher.
10: Japanese Blue
Flycatcher.

build a typical songbird nest of a cup-shaped bowl of grasses and twigs, but the nest is unusual in that the flycatchers use spiders' webs to give the nest cohesion.

To sing like a lark is a proverbial compliment in many countries where these birds are common, which is to say across most of the Old World. Nearly all of the 75 species are superb songsters, producing melodious tunes of great appeal to human ears. Of all these the most charming and best known is undoubtedly the skylark, which is as familiar on the open Mongolian plains where Genghis Khan once rode as it is in tranquil British meadows. The skylark's popularity is due as much to its aerobatics as to its magnificent song.

Though the male skylark is liable to give voice at any time of year, it does so most often during the spring. At this time the bird is anxious both to warn other males from its territory and to attract females for breeding. Taking to the wing from the grass, the skylark climbs steeply to a height of several hundred feet when it almost disappears from human view. Throughout the climb the bird pours forth its charming, rippling song. He will hover for some minutes, singing continuously, before plunging earthwards once again whereupon the song is cut short. The process may be repeated time and again throughout the days of spring. The antics of the skylark has made it a favourite subject for poets, which has served only to increase its reputation.

The larks are an easily recognisable group of songbirds for they have a number of features which mark them out from others of the group. Most noticeable is the hind toe which carries an enormously elongated, slightly curved claw. This claw is rather inconvenient for perching, but makes the larks more accomplished runners than most of the order.

As a group the larks are rather more common in the warmer regions of Africa than elsewhere, though northern species tend to stay in one area rather than be migratory. Only one species, the horned lark, is native to the New World where it ranges throughout much of the United States and exists in isolated pockets in South America. A colony of introduced skylarks is thriving on Canada's Vancouver Island.

Wherever they live, the larks inhabit grasslands or moorlands, rarely venturing into woodland or forest. Spending most of their time on the ground, the larks search for insects and their larvae, but also consume large amounts of seed and leaves. Living on open ground leaves the larks exposed to predators, so they tend to be fairly drab birds adorned with a plumage appropriate to their chosen habitat. When a large animal approaches, the larks freeze, relying on their camouflage to save them from attack. Only when about to be stepped on will the birds fly from cover and take to the air, often startling the intruder which had been unaware of its presence.

Larks have benefited from human intervention in the environment in most areas. The clearance of forest for agriculture or grazing has created ideal habitats for larks, which sing in ever greater numbers. In other ways, the larks have suffered at the hands of man, even their wonderful voices have not saved them from being extensively hunted. The ancient Romans, with their liking for ostentatious luxury served larks' tongues at their more sumptuous feasts, though this seems to have been an exceptional dish. More usual was the simple roast lark which remained in favour throughout Europe until the 17th century. In northern Europe larks were hunted by flying a hobby falcon over moorland in order to make the

larks freeze on the ground where the hawker could pick them up himself. Even today the lark is extensively hunted in many countries, most notably in Italy where small birds of many kinds are still considered delicacies.

With 54 species the pipit family, known scientifically as the motacillidae, is large as regards most avian families, but rather small compared to other songbird groups. The group is spread across almost the entire world, being found in nearly every area outside the polar regions. Within the family are two distinct types of bird, the pipits themselves and the wagtails.

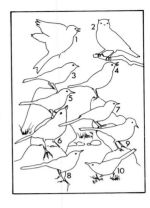

1: Skylark.
2: Shorelark.
3: Meadow Pipit.
4: Red-throated Pipit.
5: Water Pipit.
6: Yellow-throated long claw.
7: Pied Wagtail.
8: Grey Wagtail.
9: Black-backed wagtail.
10: Forest Wagtail.

Named for their song, pipits are insect-eating birds which hunt most often in open country, but may also be found in wooded areas. Some species bear a superficial resemblance to larks, not only in appearance but also in habits. The male meadow pipit, for instance, marks its territory by a singing display flight which takes the form of a steep climb, followed by a gliding descent accompanied by song. The group is occasionally known as fieldlarks.

Pipits have a habit of flicking their tails up and down, a trait seen in more extreme form in the aptly named wagtails. Coupled with the fact that wagtails are often

Top: A meadow pipit feeding a young cuckoo many times larger than itself. Cuckoos are able to lay eggs which imitate those of the host bird. Above: A pair of pied wagtails on their nest.

boldly marked and move about in the open, the tail movements make these birds highly conspicuous throughout their range which reaches across Eurasia and Africa. Wagtails show a strong preference for being close to streams, where they snap up large numbers of insects.

Inhabiting a range to the south of that of the pipits are the 120 species of bulbul which are found throughout Africa, except in the Sahara, and right across southern Asia from Turkey to Japan. The majority of these smallish birds inhabit Africa, where is found the greatest diversity of species.

As a group the bulbuls are rather plain and drab, but they have several distinctive features which mark them out from other birds. The most noticeable of these is the crest of stiff, short feathers which rises from the top of the head. Though all species tend to grow a crest, it is well developed in only a few. More universal are the small feet and short legs of the bulbuls which can appear ludicrously inappropriate in some species. In fact since the bulbuls spend most of their time on the wing or perched or roosting they have little need for strong legs to enable them to move on the ground. The birds are generally rather drab and dull in colour with shades of browns and greys. Some species, however, have bright flashes of plumage on the underside of the tail or on the cheeks.

One of these more brightly coloured bulbuls is the red-whiskered bulbul which many regard as a bird typical of the entire group. It is widely spread through India and Southeast Asia and has readily taken to areas, such as the United States, where it has been introduced by man.

Measuring around 8 inches (20 cm) in length the red-whiskered bulbul is at the smaller end of the size range for the group, for some species can reach 1 foot (30 cm). It is a conspicuous bird, not only because of its bright red flashes, but also because of its behaviour. Moving in flocks of several dozen, the bird chatters and sings loudly as it makes its way through woodland. As with most bulbuls, the red-whiskered species feeds chiefly on fruits. Using its sharp beak to bite out juicy mouthsful,

the bird gorges itself on any berries or fruit it comes across, whether it is ripe or not. It does not ignore other sources of food and may consume insects when the opportunity presents itself. The fruit diet of the bulbul makes it unpopular with farmers who regard it as a pest. It has been more successful in winning friends in cities where its ability to live alongside humans and its lively action has endeared it to many.

Like other bulbuls, the red-whiskered lays its eggs in a hollow, circular nest woven out of grass and leaves which is constructed in the branches of a tree or bush. About 4 eggs are laid and incubated by the female. The male takes over the nest for brief periods only, but is an attentive

Below: A blue tit. Bottom: A long-tailed tit on its nest. This species is found from Ireland to Japan, but numerous local variations in colouring occur across this immense range.

mate feeding the female throughout incubation.

Commonly placed close to the bulbuls are the birds of the family irenidae, which go by a variety of common names including bluebird, iora and leafbird. In many ways these birds are similar to the bulbuls, but are easily distinguished by their brilliant plumage, with yellows, reds and greens being common.

Despite being known by such a large number of common names, the family numbers only 14 species found in Southeast Asia. They inhabit the dense forests and, like bulbuls, move in noisy groups in search of fruit and nectar, though they will take invertebrate prey as well.

The common iora is found in India and Malaysia as well as on the islands of Java, Sumatra and fringing islets. It feeds on insects more than is usual for the group and is a common visitor to urban and suburban gardens where it is welcome for its depredations among insect pests. The gold-fronted leafbird, though sharing the same range as the iora is seen far less often. It is a creature of the jungles, living amongst the dense foliage and so earning

1: Red-whiskered Bulbul.
2: Long-tailed Tit.
3: Crested Tit.
4: Blue Tit.
5: Black-capped Chickadee.
6: Golden-fronted Leafbird.
7: Fairy Bluebird.
8: Common Iora.
9: European Wren.

its name. It feeds on nectar as well as on fruits and insects. The much larger fairy bluebird is rarely seen in the islands, but is widespread through India and Southeast Asia. Like the bluebird, it feeds on fruit and nectar but is usually found near running water for it drinks often.

The wrens are a family of New World birds which has one species present in the Old World. Although aberrant in distribution, the European wren is otherwise fairly typical of the family. At 4 inches (10 cm) long it is rather small and has dull brown plumage with striped markings. It lives in hedgerows and in the denser patches of woodland undergrowth, where its small size puts it at an advantage. It hunts for insects and other invertebrates but will also feast on seeds, particularly during the winter.

During the opening of the breeding season, the male wren may build several nests to which he then attracts a female. The female chooses one of the nests, lines it and lays her eggs. While the female incubates the eggs, the male occupies one of the other nests returning to help feed the nestlings. When food in plentiful a second batch of eggs is laid while the male takes the fledglings to a secondary nest and cares for them there.

Another family of small birds is the paridae, known colloquially as tits or titmice. Some scientists treat the three sub-families of the paridae as distinct families in their own right, but such a classification is far from common. The tits tend to be highly active and intelligent birds which are adept at acrobatics in the search for food. The tits feed on insects, consuming vast quantities during the breeding season to maintain themselves and their large broods. During the winter, when insects are scarce, tits feed more on seeds and fruits. They are among the first birds to feed at man-made bird tables and are especially admired by humans because of their acrobatics while seeking out food.

All the songbirds are skilful nest-builders. Their intricately woven nests are what most people think of

when describing birds' nests. Most species restrict their nest building to what is absolutely necessary to protect their blind, naked chicks during the first few weeks of life when they are particularly vulnerable to attack.

One group of songbirds, however, has taken architectural skills to the pinnacle of development, producing structures of amazing complexity and size. The bowerbirds take their name from these outstanding structures, though it is worth bearing in mind that the bowers are not nests at all, but structures designed to help mating displays.

The bower is the product and domain of the male bird which produce them. The elaborate bowers are carefully tended, being cleaned and repaired every day. In the dramatic setting of the bower, the male bird displays to passing females. When a female is attracted the male continues to display and chase her until she allows him to mate. Once mating is over the pair separate. The female flies off to construct a nest which is fairly typical of songbirds and entirely unlike the male's spectacular bower. The male, meanwhile, remains in its bower. It is thought that the male continues to attract mates, taking no interest in his offspring at all.

The family is conventionally divided into four groups on the basis of the bower style. The first, often known as catbirds, do not build a bower at all, relying instead on more conventional mating tactics. The simplest bowers are constructed by the birds known as stage-makers. These 3 species simply clear a circular area of the forest floor, some 5 feet (1.6 metres) in diameter and cover it with leaves. The male then calls from in or above his circle. These birds are among the best callers of all the bowerbirds, perhaps making up the for lack of elaboration in their bowers.

The maypole bower builders, as their name suggests, base their structures around a vertical support, usually a sapling. This upright is surrounded by a tangle of twigs and moss which may reach over 6 feet (2 metres) in height. Around this a circular patch of ground is cleared

Top left: a superb blue wren peeks out from its nest near Macquarie in New South Wales, Australia. Above: A regent bowerbird collecting material for its bower.

of debris and surrounded by a small barrier of twigs. The open space is planted with mosses and decorated with picked flowers, which are replaced when they wilt. Some species construct more elaborate structures with a thatched roof reaching between the central support to a nearby sapling or shrub.

The most intricate display stages of all are those built by the nine species of birds which produce avenue bowers. These structures are rather smaller then the maypole bowers, but are more elaborately constructed. First the male clears a patch of ground over 3 feet (1 metre) in diameter. This is then built up into a large platform of twigs as much as 1 foot (30 cm) or more in height. In the centre of this is built the 'avenue' a pair of walls made of twigs and grass which run close together to form a tunnel or avenue. The avenue may run right across the platform and have walls 18 inches (45 cm) high. Across the platform the bird scatters bright objects, such as flowers, leaves and even scraps of material and pieces of jewellery if it can get them. Perhaps the most extraordinary feature of the avenue bowers is the fact that the male bird uses a tool in decorating them. After mixing up a paint made of saliva and bright powders, the bird uses a leaf to distribute the 'paint' around the bower. Very few other birds use tools, and none for decoration.

As a group the bowerbirds are highly restricted, being found only in Australia and New Guinea. There are usually said to be 18 species of bowerbird, though there may be a nineteenth species. If the golden-fronted bowerbird still lives it must be very rare for only three specimens have ever been reported, none since the First World War. They feed in the upper branches where they seek out fruits and seeds, and some insects.

Sharing an almost identical range with the bowerbirds are the colourful birds of paradise. These magnificent

birds take their name from the incredible beauty of the male's breeding plumage which has been held to be so spectacular that the birds would be suitable inhabitants of paradise.

The birds of paradise are grouped together in the family paradisaeidae, which shows many similarities to the bowerbirds. The variations between the groups are restricted to details such as the relative lengths of foot bones. However, the behavioural and visual differences between the two families is so great that it justifies the existence of two families. While the bowerbirds have developed the habit of building display grounds to attract females, the birds of paradise have developed almost unbelievably elaborate display plumes and some remarkable dances. More than one species will hang upside down from branches and swing gently while waving their feathers.

The magnificence and vivid hues of the plumage of these birds is truly astounding, and naturalists have long sought an explanation for the wild variations to be found in this group. The birds of paradise are, after all, a fairly small family of birds with a highly restricted range, some species being found only on a few small islands. Some have suggested that the dim light which filters down through the forest canopy would make duller coloured birds difficult to see. The bright plumage would therefore act as a beacon to other birds during the mating season. Though this fact undoubtedly played a part in the development of the showy feathers, there is probably more to it than that.

Birds of paradise are polygamous, that is the male will mate with a number of different females during the season. The females then build the nest and care for the young on their own and without any help from the male. Added to this is the fact that many species are so closely related that crossbreeding is possible, though it produces sterile offspring. Clearly there could be great confusion between the species at mating time, with males pursuing any likely female and so producing large numbers of sterile offspring. Some recognition device was necessary to stop wasteful nesting activities and to ensure the survival of the species.

It was probably this which led to the evolution of the magnificent plumage. The females are dull, brown birds which appear much alike, but they seem to be instinctively attracted to the pattern of feathers found on the male of their species. When a male bird displays he will attract females of his own species, but be ignored by those of other species. Natural selection would tend to favour those males with the more exaggerated plumage patterns, so producing the colourful displays which are present in today's birds.

Though the birds of paradise inhabit remote and treacherous countryside, including swamps and forests, their plumes have ensured that they are a widely known, if poorly studied, group. In fact the first European to visit the area, Ferdinand Magellan in 1522, was so impressed by the birds that he took two skins back with him to show his fellow countrymen as examples of the wonders of the Indies. Later travellers also collected plumes, but it was not until the 19th century that the trade developed into a business. By 1900 tens of thousands of skins were being exported each year. The feather merchants in Europe were besieged by naturalists eager to discover new species of these colourful birds among the skins. They gave the birds names of their patrons, such as the King of Saxony bird of paradise and Princess Stephana's bird of paradise.

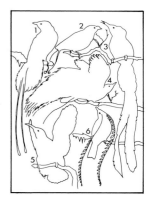

1: Prince Rudolf's Blue Bird of Paradise.
2: King Bird of Paradise.
3: Princess Stephanie's Bird of Paradise.
4: Count Reggi's Bird of Paradise.
5: Magnificent Riflebird.
6: King of Saxony's Bird of Paradise.

Left: A lesser bird of paradise in its natural jungle home, where the dense foliage and mottled shadows may obscure even the brightest of colouring.

Only one bird seems to have been named for its habits in the field, the magnificent riflebird. It gained its name from the fact that its calls sound precisely like a rifle bullet fizzing through the air.

The classification of the songbirds has long been a subject for controversy and disagreement among naturalists. The nomination for being the most advanced family of the songbirds, themselves the most advanced order of birds, has not escaped this general debate. It was once widely accepted that the three most advanced families were those of the bowerbirds, birds of paradise and crows. The first two were nominated for their advanced and complicated social lives and breeding behaviour, while the crows attracted attention due to their superior intelligence.

More recently attention has centred on the seed-eating birds known as finches. Those scientists who favour the finches point out that the bowerbirds and birds of paradise are both small families with a restricted range and relatively few species. This would indicate that these birds are specialised side branches of the evolutionary trail rather than the main stream. Doubt has also been cast on the intelligence of the crow family. The finches, it is claimed, represent the main stream of avian evolution because of their worldwide distribution and their recent and dramatic evolution into a wide variety of types. Both systems of classification are still in use in ornithological circles, so it is difficult to be certain as to

which candidate represents the true pinnacle of the bird world.

Whether or not the finches are the leaders of the birds, they are a highly diverse group counting among their number around 700 species from every continent except Antarctica. The internal divisions of the finches are unclear and defining them is generally treated with some reservation. It is not even certain that all the finches arose from a single ancestral stock of primitive birds, or whether they represent a number of quite separate lines of descent which have come to resemble each other through adapting to a similar lifestyle.

As a group, the finches tend to be fairly small birds which are highly active and have a tendency towards colourful and showy plumage. The most distinctive feature of the group, however, is to be found in the beak. Most species are specialised to deal with a particular food source. This usually involves extricating a seed from the parent plant which is not always an easy task.

The colourful red cardinal of North America has what might be termed a standard finch beak which is short and squat, and takes up much of the bird's face. The red cardinal feeds on berries and various seeds, needing a beak able to deal with these sources. The European goldfinch has a more pointed beak and feeds upon small seeds, such as those of the dandelion and thistle. More specialised is the bill of the crossbill, the tips of which overlap considerably. This peculiar bill is used to winkle seeds out of fir cones. Some finches have enormously powerful bills and are able to crack open protective casings as tough as that which surrounds a cherry stone.

Below: A pair of bullfinches feeding their young in the nest built in a wild rose bush.
Below left: A chaffinch.
Bottom: A summer tanager in the Sonoran Desert.

1: *American Goldfinch.*
2: *Red Cardinal.*
3: *Diamond Firetail Finch.*
4: *Bullfinch.*
5: *Golden Oriole.*
6: *Scarlet Tanager.*
7: *Chaffinch.*
8: *Baltimore Oriole.*
9: *European Goldfinch.*
10: *Snowfinch.*

TURTLES AND TORTOISES
Armoured Reptiles

Despite the fact that the tortoises and turtles, the chelonians, have possibly the most specialised and unusual body plan of any reptile they are generally reckoned to be among the most primitive. All reptiles are classified according to the structure of their skulls. Some groups have large 'windows' or openings in their skulls in order to lighten the structure without reducing its strength. It is the arrangement and number of these windows and their position in relation to the bones which determines the basic classification of the reptiles. Chelonians have no windows at all.

The chelonians are a remarkably old reptile order which has scarcely changed since it first appeared in the fossil record. The oldest fossil chelonian so far known is *Proganochelys* which lived in Germany around 200 million years ago, some 90 million years after the reptiles first evolved. No earlier creatures are known which could have been an ancestor of this creature, so the ancestry of the chelonians is unknown.

Although it is the earliest known chelonian, *Proganochelys* was already a fully formed tortoise which had many of the features typical of the modern land chelonians. It had a fully formed shell, made up of a domed carapace across the back and a plastron covering the belly. As in modern tortoises the shell was made up of a number of bony knobs covered by large, flat plates of shell. Indeed the ancient tortoise had rather more shell plates than modern species, with several side plates protecting the legs.

Internally, the backbone of the first tortoise had just 10 vertebrae which were fully fused to the carapace, another unique feature of modern chelonians. The few ribs were likewise attached to the shell. Almost the only way in which this earliest tortoise differed from modern creatures was that it could not retract its head and legs in order to protect them within the shell. The head had strong jaws, but they bore no teeth. Presumably the creature had a tough horny beak like that of present day species.

The method used by modern chelonians when retracting their heads has come to be used as a system of classification. Those which kink their necks in a vertical plane to retract the head are known as the cryptodira and contain about 180 species. Another group, of just 49 species, kink their necks horizontally and are termed pleurodira.

The 40 or so species of land chelonian, generally known as tortoises, are so similar as to be placed within a single family, the testudinidae. Easily the largest of these is the aptly named giant tortoise, which can grow to over 4 feet (1.2 metres) in length and tip the scales at 600 lbs (275 kg). These creatures are restricted to various islands in the Indian Ocean, particularly the Seychelles and Galapagos. It is presumed that the tortoises were able to become so large on these islands because of a lack of competition from other animals.

Since around 1500 the islands where giant tortoises live have been visited regularly by European ships. Early mariners hunted the tortoises relentlessly, exterminating them on some islands. Other sailors, recognising the value of islands well stocked with tortoises, introduced the creatures to islands previously without them. No records of such acts were kept, so as a result it is now impossible to be certain which islands were the original homes of the various sub-species.

The vast majority of land tortoises are strictly vegetarian, only a few species taking small amounts of animal food. To cope with this food a large gut is needed, and it is this which largely fills the domed carapace. The legs tend to be solid and heavy, as they need to bear the weight of the shell as well as that of the body. When danger threatens the tortoises withdraw their heads and legs, leaving only the shell and tough scales visible to predators. As the creatures rely on armour for defence they do to attempt to flee when disturbed and can be approached easily.

The aquatic chelonians are known collectively as turtles, although common names such as terrapin and matamata abound. The body plan is very similar to that of tortoises, but the stout legs are replaced by long, slender flippers for swimming.

Snapping turtles grow to around 2 feet (60 cm) in length and are dedicated carnivores. They rest on the bottom of rivers with their mouths agape. A small pink lobe in the mouth is wiggled to attract fish. When a victim approaches, the turtle snaps with its razor sharp beak. Small prey are swallowed in one, but larger fish may be cut in half by the first, swift bite. Other freshwater turtles are more vegetarian, with most having a fairly mixed diet.

The green turtle is perhaps typical of the large marine species, it is certainly the most intensively studied. Measuring around 4 feet (1.2 metres) in length the green turtle is a heavy creature, but when swimming most of its weight is supported by the water, allowing the turtle to move freely. When the breeding season begins, the turtles migrate to the offshore waters of certain special nesting beaches. The female then hauls herself up on to the beach, moving laboriously because of her great weight. A shallow hole is dug with the flippers and in this the 100 or so eggs are laid. The female then covers these over before returning to the sea. Left alone, the eggs are kept warm by the sun and hatch after about 70 days. The dozens of tiny turtles dash for the sea, but the majority are snapped up by waiting birds within the first few seconds of life. Only a minority survive to adulthood.

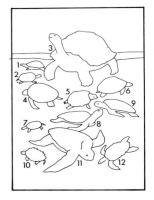

1: *Margined Tortoise.*
2: *Spanish Terrapin.*
3: *Giant Tortoise.*
4: *Green Turtle.*
5: *Red-eared Turtle.*
6: *Herman's Tortoise.*
7: *Snapper Turtle.*
8: *Long-eared Turtle.*
9: *Flat-back Turtle.*
10: *Alligator Turtle.*
11: *Leathery Turtle.*
12: *Hawksbill Turtle.*

Left: A star tortoise of Sri Lanka which takes its name from the striking markings on the upper carapace.

CROCODILES
Swamp Predators

Crocodiles and alligators are, without doubt, extremely aggressive and powerful beasts of prey which make their homes in swamps and rivers throughout the tropical regions of the world. They are, however, surpassed by closely allied reptiles which became extinct many millions of years ago. Crocodilians belong to the group of reptiles known as archosaurs which are characterised not only by having two windows, or openings, in the skull but also by having their teeth set in individual sockets, unlike most reptiles which have all their teeth growing from a single groove.

About 220 million years ago the archosaurs spread and evolved rapidly to produce three groups. The first developed wings and became the flying pterosaurs. The second increased dramatically in size and improved their limbs to become the mighty dinosaurs. The third group remained little altered and gave rise to the crocodilians. The body plan of crocodilians has remained remarkably unchanged since. Indeed the group is the sole survivor of the great reptiles of the Age of Dinosaurs.

Crocodilians are typically large, heavy bodied creatures with strongly muscled legs. Unlike other reptiles, crocodilians are able to lift their bodies clear of the ground on their legs in order to run at high speed for short distances. The hind feet are webbed, but most locomotive power in the water is provided by the tail. This limb is exceptionally long and muscular and is flattened longitudinally in order to give better purchase on the water. Using the tail, crocodilians can move extremely quickly when hunting.

As active predators, the crocodilians need a formidable array of weapons with which to subdue their prey. For this they are well equipped with long jaws filled with sharp pointed teeth and powered by strong muscles. Crocodilians are capable of dealing with any creature smaller than themselves and have earned a reputation as formidable killers. A favourite hunting ploy is to lurk beneath the surface and slowly approach creatures come to drink. With a final rush, the crocodilians dash out of the water to seize a victim and drag it back below the surface. Most species will kill larger prey by holding them beneath the water until they drown. The carcasses are often stored under logs or rocks until they begin to decompose. For all their jaw power, crocodilians are unable to bite chunks from a fresh carcass or to chew their food. They need to bolt their food whole or to wait for time to soften it.

Unlike the vast majority of reptiles, crocodilians are good parents, caring for their young until they are old enough to fend for themselves. Before laying the two dozen or so eggs, the female constructs a mound of vegetation near the water's edge. The eggs are laid deep in the mound so that the warmth produced by the decaying vegetation keeps them at a suitable temperature. The mother guards the nest against intruders during incubation, sometimes sleeping on the nest. Once the young are hatched the mother carries them to water and then continues to keep an eye on them for some days.

The largest of all the crocodilians is the estuarine crocodile of Indonesia and northern Australia. These formidable beasts average around 16 feet (5 metres) but large males may top 28 feet (8.5 metres). These huge creatures spend more time in the water than other species and patrol some distance out to sea. They feed upon fish and other aquatic life, though they do not hesitate to attack terrestrial animals when given the chance. Estuarine crocodiles have been known to attack humans without provocation, treating them as they would any other potential prey. In one notorious incident in World War II, estuarine crocodiles are reported to have devoured an entire Japanese battalion trapped in a swamp by British troops.

Below: A mugger crocodile in Sri Lanka. Bottom: The open jaws of a Nile Crocodile.

The alligators, or caimans, can be distinguished from the crocodiles in a number of ways. Perhaps the most noticeable are related to the snout, which is shorter, broader and blunter than that of crocodiles. Like crocodiles, the alligators have an exceptionally large pair of teeth near the front of the lower jaw. When an alligator closes its mouth these teeth fit into pits in the upper jaw and so cannot be seen as can those of the crocodile.

The largest alligator is the American alligator, found only in the Florida Everglades, the Louisiana bayous and similar marshy habitats of the southern United States. It grows to around 16 feet (5 metres) and has been known to attack humans. This alligator spends most of its time resting on river banks, entering the water to feed.

The single species of gharial, or gavial, can be distinguished by the pronounced bulb on the tip of its snout. It inhabits the Ganges and Indus, and their larger tributaries, and is totally dependant on a diet of fish. Its jaws lack the huge conical teeth of alligators and crocodiles, having instead dozens of small, needle-sharp teeth, which are ideal for catching small, slippery fish.

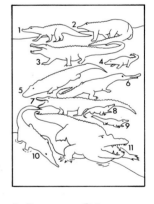

1: Paraguayan Caiman.
2: False Gharial.
3: Mississippi Alligator.
4: Speckled Caiman.
5: Black Crocodile.
6: Gharial.
7: Nile Crocodile.
8: Smooth-fronted Caiman.
9: African Pygmy Crocodile.
10: Australian Freshwater Crocodile.
11: Estuarine Crocodile.

GECKOS
The Wall Walkers

With something over 500 species, the geckos are amongst the largest of the lizard groups. The various species are found throughout the warmer areas of the world, flourishing in a variety of habitats. Geckos may inhabit forests, swamps, deserts or plains, with several species co-existing with ease. Indeed, the only controlling factor seems to be the number of insects, on which most geckos feed. Where these creatures are plentiful, geckos are numberous, but where insects are absent, the geckos are rare.

Geckos are generally considered to be amongst the more primitive of the lizards for they have a number of unspecialised features. They have five, or sometimes four, digits on each foot thus linking them to the earliest of all the lizards which lived over 200 million years ago. Geckos tend to be rather small, rarely measuring more than a foot (30 cm) in length and most species being under 8 inches (20 cm). The head and body tend to be rather flat, enabling the gecko to cling to the ground inconspicuously.

This latter ability is of great use to the geckos. They have no scales on the upper surfaces of their body and are therefore highly vulnerable to attack. In addition to this lack of body armour, the geckos habitually spend long periods of time in exposed positions. Loving warmth, the geckos bask in the sunshine for long hours every day. In part this serves the purpose of raising the gecko's body temperature so that it is able to remain active during its nocturnal forays in search of prey. By pressing its body flat against the surface on which it rests, the gecko ensures that it casts as small a shadow as is possible. This makes it less easily seen by passing predators and so less likely to be attacked.

The ability of geckos to press themselves flat is taken to the extreme by the leaf-tailed gecko of Madagascar. This forest lizard has a broad tail which, when laid flat, is virtually indistinguishable from the bark on which the creature habitually rests. The flanks and limbs are fringed with long scales which help the body merge with its surroundings. It also has the ability to change its coloration slightly in order to blend in with its background more completely.

If a gecko is spotted it has several abilities which aid attempts at escape. The long tail which most geckos carry trails behind it as it runs. Not unnaturally it is the tail which is usually seized first by a pursuer. When this happens, the gecko is able to contract tail muscles violently, so breaking the tail near its base. The hunter is left with the tail while the gecko makes good its escape. Over the following weeks, the gecko grows a new tail. In most species regenerated tails are more stumpy and less elegant than the original.

Should the tail-breaking trick not be sufficient to shake off a pursuer, geckos can exhibit amazing agility in fleeing danger. Moving with all the speed and darting movements typical of lizards, geckos may dash for crevices or cracks in which to hide. They are also able to climb on surfaces which would be utterly impassable to other creatures. These climbing skills are also displayed when the gecko is hunting.

Geckos are often seen scampering up vertical walls and will even walk upside down across ceilings, apparently oblivious both to their inverted position and the long drop beneath them. Geckos have even been seen to scamper up window panes and to cling unconcernedly to polished metals. It used to be thought that this proficiency was due to small sucker pads located on the undersides of the toes. Only this, it was thought, would allow the creatures to scamper across smooth, polished surfaces. More recently microscopic examination of the feet has shown the toes to be covered, not with suction pads, but with thousands of tiny hooks. It is these which provide grip, finding enough irregularity to gain a hold on even the smoothest surfaces.

Most geckos are active at night, the diurnal gecko being a rare exception. Because they move in the darkness, geckos are often difficult to see, but they can be heard much more easily. Possibly the loudest of all reptiles, geckos habitually emit loud calls, repeated over and over again. The very name 'gecko' came from the clicking sound which the creatures emit. The common names of many individual species being likewise derived from their call.

The vast majority of geckos are strict carnivores and include insects as an important part of their diet. The larger species, such as the tokay of southern Asia, also prey on larger creatures. Other lizards may be taken, as may fledgling birds or rodents. Unlike most geckos the tokay is liable to fight back if threatened, inflicting nasty bites.

1: Flying Gecko.
2: Leaf-tailed Gecko.
3: Burrowing Gecko.
4: Banded Gecko.
5: Diurnal Gecko.
6: Yellow-headed Gecko.
7: South American Gecko.
8: Tockay Gecko.

Above: A New Zealand gecko of the genus Heteropholis. Left: A hatchling of the gecko genus Hemidactlyus in Kenya's Tsavo National Park.

AGAMID LIZARDS
The Fat Lizards

With around 3,000 species the lizards are far and away the most successful group of reptiles alive today. They have produced a vast number of variations with species being adapted to swimming, running and even gliding. Though they exhibit so many specialisations, the lizards have maintained a fairly constant body plan since they evolved some 250 million years ago.

They are generally elongated creatures, often with immensely long tails, and narrow heads carried on highly mobile necks. The legs are splayed outwards from the body with the shins turned downwards to meet the ground. When at rest, most lizards have their bellies flat on the ground for it takes considerable muscular effort to lift the body on to the legs. This compares with the leg layout of birds and mammals where vertically arranged bones take the weight.

Taxonomically, the lizards are placed in the same order as the snakes. Although the two groups are different in many respects, the snakes clearly evolved from the lizards and share several specific features which distinguish them from all other reptiles. The two most important of these features are to be found in the structure of the head. The most immediately obvious is that a section of skull found in other reptiles is missing in the lizards and snakes. In its place are large, bulging muscles which operate the jaws with much greater force than would be possible otherwise. The second unique feature is that the skull bones themselves are jointed, allowing a slight flexibility in the upper jaw, which is rigid in most other vertebrates.

One of the most primitive groups of lizard is the agamid lizard, which includes around 300 species found throughout much of Europe, Africa, Asia and Australia. Within this range they are absent only from colder regions or offshore islands such as Madagascar and New Zealand. They have a thick tongue with teeth arranged along the outside of the jaw. The vast majority of species are active during the day and may spend long periods of time basking in the sunshine to soak up warmth. As cold-blooded creatures, the lizards are unable to produce internal heat to maintain their metabolic functions. The highly active lifestyle of the agamids makes it essential that they absorb enough warmth from the sun.

The body plan of the agamids is highly variable, but usually conforms to a basic standard. The body itself tends to be fairly plump and broad and may be decorated with crests and flaps of colourful scales. The head is triangular in profile, coming to a sharp point at the tip of the snout. The tail is fairly long and thin, but not as pronounced as in some other groups.

The reptiles of the genus Agama are perhaps the most typical of the entire group. The hardun, a lizard of the Near East and the Balkans, is generally found in hilly and mountainous areas where bare rocks are plentiful. It uses the numerous cracks and crevices of the stone as hiding places, emerging to bask in the sunlight and hunt insects. Reaching a total length of around 16 inches (40 cm) the hardun is a moderately sized agamid, but it is not easy to see. Its dull coloration enables it to blend into the background, while its ability to run at high speed allows it to dash into hiding as soon as danger threatens.

Measuring only 4 inches (10 cm) in length the common agama is small for its family but has a highly developed social life. The creatures live in small groups, rarely numbering more than two dozen, which are led by an adult male. The male holds a rigidly defined territory which he defends vigorously. When another male intrudes, the resident immediately reacts by engaging in the fighting display. Lifting his sky blue head to reveal a throat of orange and blue stripes, he bobs and ducks repeatedly in order to flash colours at the intruder. The male is noted for its ability to change its skin colour rapidly. The head bobbing continues until one or other rival backs down.

Several species of agamid are known as dragons and are adorned with crests and spines. The 2 foot (60 cm) long eastern water dragon is a native of eastern Australia where it inhabits forested areas, close to water. It habitually favours the branches of trees and bushes which overhang streams or lakes. If it feels threatened, perhaps by a bird or snake, the eastern water dragon flings itself off the branch into the water below and swims off rapidly. The creature is equally adept at hunting on land or in water. A large proportion of its diet is made up of frogs and fish, though it readily snaps up insects both in the water and on land.

The bearded dragon shares the same geographical range as the eastern water dragon, but prefers drier habitats, even venturing into areas of semi-desert. At 18 inches (45 cm) it is fairly large, and its appearance is made all the more impressive by the fact that its scales are enlarged into long, pointed spines across much of its body. The scales around the neck and throat are particularly large and can be erected into an impressive frill, which has given the creature its name. Like the eastern water dragon, the bearded dragon includes a proportion of fruit in its diet.

More impressive neck adornments are to be seen in the frilled lizards of Australia. These creatures have fairly small bodies, with elongated tails which may account for two thirds of the overall length. Frilled lizards hunt for insects and small vertebrates in forested areas. They would be an easy prey to larger creatures, but have developed a remarkable defence mechanism. When threatened, the creature faces the danger and opens its mouth wide, erecting at the same time a large frill of skin around its neck. This has the effect of increasing the animal's size enormously and is often enough to frighten off intruders.

Even more impressive are the flying dragons of Indonesia and Southeast Asia. Measuring about 12 inches (30 cm) in length the flying dragons are fairly typical agamids as regards diet and habitat, but indulge in highly unusual behaviour. The flying dragons live in rainforest trees and will readily leap from one tree to another, over long distances. As soon as it takes to the air, the dragon unfolds long flaps of skin along its flanks which act as gliding wings which enable the reptile to cover long distances before it reaches the ground or a fresh perch. The 'wings' are, in fact, abnormally elongated ribs covered with webbed skin and cannot be flapped so making sustained flight impossible. When not in the air, the 'wings' are folded against the body and merge into the background. When opened, however, they often reveal brightly coloured flashes of skin.

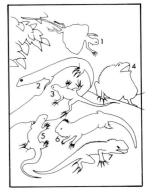

1: *Flying Dragon.*
2: *Desert Night Lizard.*
3: *Common Agama.*
4: *Dragon.*
5: *Butterfly Lizard.*
6: *Bearded Dragon.*
7: *Rainforest Dragon.*

IGUANAS
Last of the Sea Lizards

Millions of years ago there was a far greater diversity of lizards than exists today. One group abandoned the land for a life in the sea, evolving fins and tails. These were the mosasaurs, of which the largest *Tylosaurus* was over 26 feet (8 metres) in length. Such monsters are long since gone, and today only one lizard is associated with the sea.

The marine iguana is smaller than *Tylosaurus*, but is still impressive with an overall length of 5 feet (1.6 metres). It is an increasingly rare creature for its territory has been invaded by domestic dogs and cats which feed extensively on the iguanas. Before the arrival of these animals on the isolated Galapagos Islands off the South American Pacific coast, the marine iguanas had no natural enemies. They were to be found in vast numbers around the coasts of the islands, basking on rocks and beaches while they soaked up the warmth of the sun.

When low tide reveals the extensive beds of seaweed on the submerged rocks, the marine iguanas clamber down to browse on the vegetation. Occasionally an iguana will take to the water in search of fresh pastures, perhaps striking out for a neighbouring island. They are strong swimmers, using their long muscular tails to push themselves through the water.

The closely related land iguana which also lives on the Galapagos Islands is a very similar animal, though its body is rather stouter and rounder. It frequents the drier areas of the islands, feeding on cacti and other plants.

The two iguanas from the Galapagos Islands are rather untypical of the group, which includes some 600 species. Most iguanas live in trees or on the ground, though a few burrow, and feed almost exclusively on insects and other small animals. Nearly all the species are found in the New World and on associated islands, though a few occur on isolated islands like Fiji and Madagascar. It has been noted that this uneven distribution means that iguanas are never fund in the same range as agamid lizards. It has been conjectured that the two groups, similar in appearance and habits, are direct competitors for the same niche in life. If the two were to meet it is likely they would dispute the same food sources and habitat with one gradually driving the other to extinction.

Iguanas vary greatly in size for although the majority of species are small and lightly built, the common iguana of Venezuelan forests may be over 6 feet (2 metres) in length and is a heavily built creature.

Most species sport spines or crests in one shape or another, a feature taken to an extreme in the basilisk of South America. The males of this fast, lightly built

species have tall crests along their backs and over the root of the tail. The skull is decorated with solid bony flanges. It is thought that the various growths are associated with breeding. Only the males sport them and each species of basilisk has a slightly different shape of crest. Presumably these allow females to identify a male of the correct species as they are otherwise indistinguishable. Basilisks have the unusual ability of being able to walk on water. They frequent riverside locations and are rarely far from open water. Using its tail as a counterweight, a basilisk can run on its hind legs at great speed. So fast is the top speed, that the lizard is able to keep moving without breaking the surface tension of water. After a few paces, however, the creature normally slows down and, breaking through the surface, swims in a more normal fashion.

Like several other types of lizard, the iguanas have the ability to change colour, though in the iguanas it is rather limited. The base colour of most iguanas is green, but brown pigment cells are able to mask the green or blend with it to produce shades of grey and green at will. The effect is produced by the brown pigment within the cells moving between the surface, where it can be seen, and deep in the cell where it cannot. A few species are able to produce violent red flushes by subduing the brown pigment and pushing blood through surface capillaries to show the colour of the blood.

Many species have elaborate courtships. The physical adornments of the basilisks are shared, in less spectacular fashion, by many other iguanas. Males will mark out a breeding territory in which they will tolerate no other male. An invading rival will be driven off with vigorous displays and threats. Equally impressive shows may be put on by the males when attracting a female. The females of many species dig holes or burrow into dead vegetation to construct nesting sites. Clutches of between 3 and 36 eggs are laid and then abandoned. A few species lay single eggs at intervals throughout the breeding season. The young hatch out several weeks later and have to find their way in the world at once.

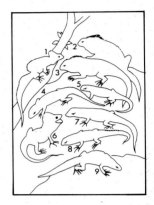

1: *Colombian Iguana.*
2: *Marine Iguana.*
3: *Land Iguana.*
4: *Spiny-tailed Iguana.*
5: *South American Iguana.*
6: *Crested Iguana.*
7: *Mottled Iguana.*
8: *Caribbean Iguana.*
9: *Mexican Iguana.*

Left: A marine iguana sunning itself on the rocks of the Galapagos Islands. Below: The type species known scientifically as Iguana Iguana and more usually as the common iguana.

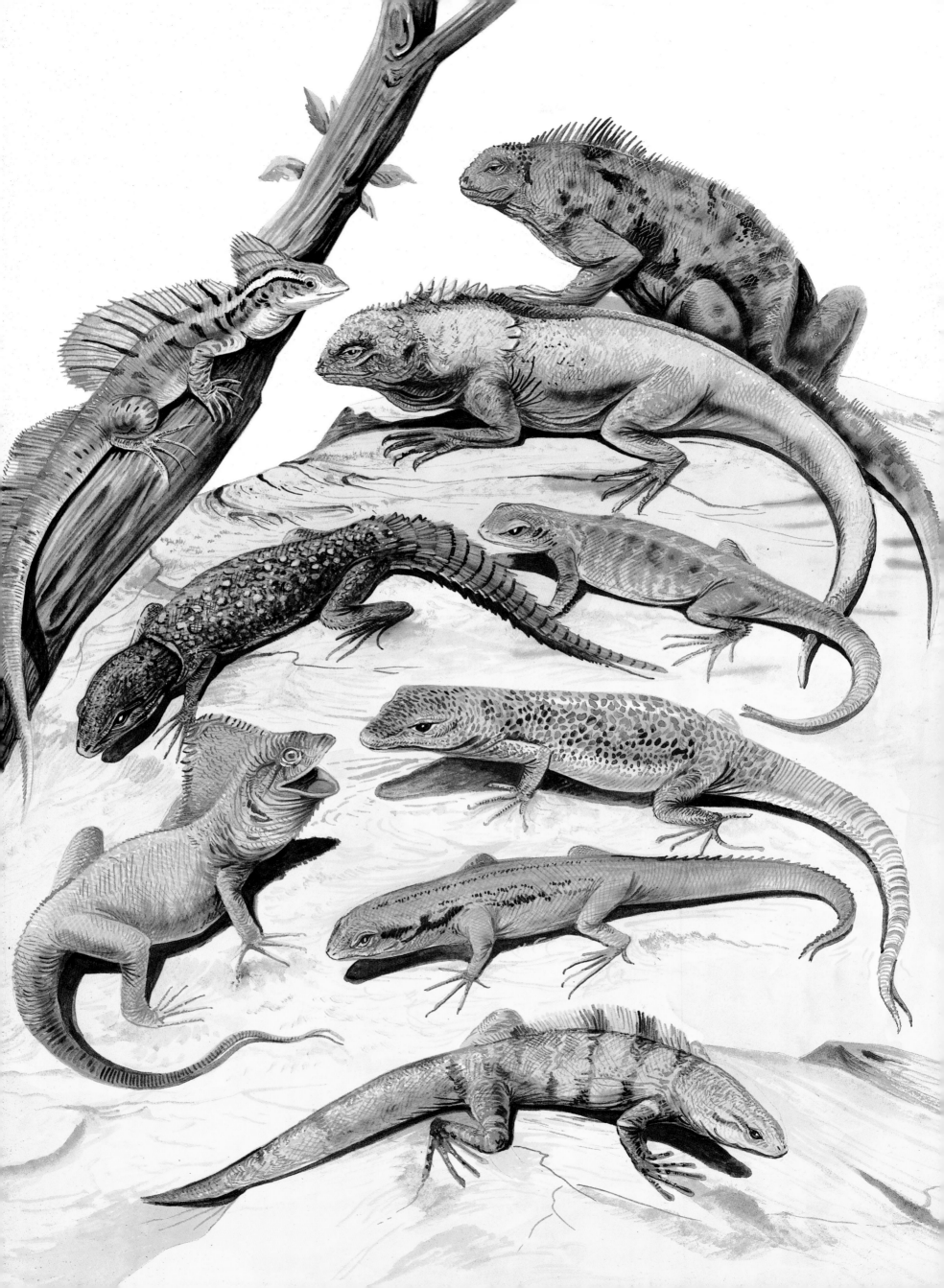

MONITORS
The Hunting Lizards

Most lizards are hunters in one way or another, but none can match the monitors in sheer ferocity and power. The larger species are well able to bring down an ox while even the smallest rarely hesitate to attack creatures of a comparable size. So aggressive are monitors that when they are kept in captivity they are almost invariably held in solitary confinement to prevent them attacking and eating other exhibits.

All monitors conform to a similar body plan, the most notable characteristic of which is size. The smallest species are usually around 6 feet (2 metres) in length while the longest reaches over 15 feet (4.7 metres). The two longest species are very different, the Salvadori monitor is a lithe, slim beast while the aptly named

Komodo dragon is a huge, heavy beast able to tackle large mammals with ease. Unconfirmed reports mention Komodo dragons reaching lengths of over 25 feet (8 metres).

Despite the variation in size most species of monitor are fairly similar in basic body plan. They are long-bodied lizards with long, muscular tails and stout legs. The feet carry long, sharp claws which are used when attacking prey. The head, carried on a flexible neck, is flat and blunt and holds jaws equipped with stout, sharp teeth. The long neck is highly mobile and can twist the head to face in almost any direction, a unique ability among lizards. The monitors use their long forked tongues to great effect, scenting out potential prey with great

accuracy. When the monitor closes for the kill, the tongue is completely withdrawn and tucked into a special sheath at the base of the mouth. This protects this essential but delicate sense organ from damage.

Though the claws and teeth are used when attacking prey, the monitors use a quite different weapon when on the defensive. When under attack, they turn to present their tails to the adversary and lash around. The heavy tail is capable of being whipped towards the enemy at high speed and, if it makes contact, can inflict severe bruising or broken bones.

Monitors are widely spread throughout the warmer regions of the Old World being found in Africa, Asia and Australasia, though like other lizards they are absent from offshore islands such as Madagascar. The group reaches its greatest range in Australia where it may have originated. Fossil monitors from Australia reach lengths far in excess of modern species, topping 25 feet (8 metres). They have become adapted to a wide variety of habitats, with some species having curved claws particularly suitable for climbing trees. Others are semi-aquatic and feature a tail flattened laterally to aid them in swimming.

The monitors reproduce by the usual reptilian method of egg-laying. The males herald the breeding season by taking part in impressive dominance contests, by rearing on to their hind legs and attempting to push each other over. After mating, the female lays her eggs in the ground where they are abandoned to hatch out several weeks later. Only the female Nile monitor has developed any attempt at egg care. She rips open a termite mound in which to lay her eggs. The termites quickly repair the damage, leaving the eggs in the nest where they remain warm and safe until the young lizards hatch out.

In Australia the monitors are known as goannas, apparently a corruption of the name iguana, and are treated with hostility by farmers. Perhaps the favourite food of monitors is eggs. The monitors eat these by delicately lifting the eggs into their mouths and manoeuvring them to the back of the mouth. The shell is then crushed and the contents sucked up while the shell is discarded.

When farmers and ranchers first moved into the Australian bush the farmers kept flocks of poultry and soon came to regard the egg-eating monitors as a definite pest. When the pressure of work allowed, the locals would gather for a 'goanna hunt'. It was during these hunts that a habit of the monitors was discovered which gave rise to much hilarity among the hunters. The monitors of Australia are partly arboreal. Whenever they are caught in the open by an intruder their first instinct is to make for the nearest tree. This is climbed by a sudden rush, after which the monitor strives to keep the trunk between itself and any potential danger.

When surprised some distance from trees, however, the monitor would dash for the nearest upright object, very often one of the human hunters. Old bush men quickly learnt to lie flat when a goanna approached, whereupon it would lose interest and could be shot. 'New chums', however, were rarely let in to the secret in the hope that they would end the hunt with a goanna on their head, much to the amusement of the bush men.

1: Gould's Goanna.
2: Spotted Tree Monitor.
3: Rough-necked Monitor.
4: Papua Monitor.
5: Golden Monitor.
6: Green Monitor.
7: Timor Monitor.
8: Varanus storri.
9: Water Monitor.

Left: A monitor lizard stalks a spitting cobra over a termite mound. The monitors are all active carnivores and will prey on many types of animal.

CHAMELEONS
The Specialist Lizards

Chameleons are without doubt the most specialised and advanced of all the lizards, with a number of features quite unlike those of other groups. The vast majority of the 85 species are found in Africa, where the group probably originated, though some have found their way to Asia and there is one species in Crete and southern Spain. The fact that chameleons are present on Madagascar, unlike many other African lizard groups might suggest that they first evolved before that island separated from Africa. This would place their separation from the basic lizard stock far back in time, perhaps around 100 million years or more.

The largest chameleon, a Madagascan species, reaches 2 feet (80 cm) in length, but most species are about one third of this length. Typically chameleons are creatures of warm or hot forests which feed exclusively on insects. The vast majority of the many specialisations of the group are directed to this lifestyle, at which the chameleons have become expert.

Adaptations for climbing in trees are typified by the tail of the chameleons. As in other lizards, the tail is long and thin, tapering gradually to a point. Unlike the tails of other lizards, however, that of the chameleon is prehensile and can be used to grip twigs and branches, providing a secure anchor for the chameleon. When not in use the tail is often carried in a tight spiral, keeping it out of danger. Other lizards frequently lose their tails to predators, an event which would be dangerous to the chameleon.

The feet are likewise specialised to gripping twigs. Each foot is divided with three toes being opposable to the other two. Together with the short but strong claws this gives the chameleon a secure grip on branches which might be thrashed about by tropical storms. As an added safeguard the chameleon has developed the habit of never lifting more than one foot at a time, ensuring that at least three feet, and perhaps the tail, are holding it secure at any one moment.

This inevitably means that the chameleons are slow moving creatures unable to flee rapidly from danger like other lizards. Instead they rely upon camouflage to protect them from danger. While moving the chameleons rock gently back and forth so as to merge in with the swaying movements of surrounding foliage, rather than betray their presence with a sustained forward motion.

Coloration is also critical to the camouflage of the chameleons and in this group the lizard colour-changing ability is brought to its pinnacle. The skin contains packets of pigment of various colours, including red, yellow, black and white. The pigment is arranged in cells which run deep beneath the skin surface. When nervous signals reach the cells, the pigments migrate to near the skin surface and become visible, or retreat to the depths and so are masked. By controlling the proportions and amounts of various pigments near the surface, the chameleon is able to control the shade and brightness of the colour of any part of its skin. Usually the colour co-ordination is chiefly dependant on the brightness of the surroundings. The chameleons alter the shade of their skins so as to fit into the background.

When hunting the chameleon relies chiefly on stealth to approach its victims and on its amazing tongue to secure a kill. While at rest, the chameleon continually searches its surroundings for a likely prey. The eyes are mounted in turrets which can be swivelled round to look in any direction. The two eyes are able to act independently of each other, allowing the chameleon to watch a large area of space. When an insect is spotted, the chameleon slowly moves toward it with slow, deliberate, swaying paces until the chameleon has positioned itself to face the prey at a certain range.

Once it is satisfied that all is ready, the chameleon launches its attack, which is so rapid that it often escapes the eye and gives the lie to the reptile's characteristic slowness. The tongue of the chameleon flashes out, slaps against the insect and drags it back into the mouth. The whole action can be over in less than one tenth of a second.

The tongue is perhaps the most specialised feature of the chameleon. It is extremely muscular and elastic, being hollow for most of its length and attached to pivoted plates within the mouth. Usually the tongue is carried in the mouth protected by a bony plate. When about to strike, the plate is slid aside and the tongue brought up behind the lips. The chameleon's lines itself up, then launches the tongue by rapidly contracting circular muscles within the stalk and shifting the supporting base plates. The solid tip of the tongue is covered with a sticky secretion which entraps the insect prey as soon as it touches. The retraction of the tongue is aided by its elasticity and by muscular action.

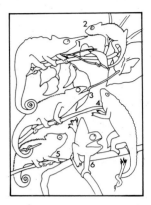

1: *Mountain Chameleon.*
2: *Pygmy Chameleon.*
3: *Flap-necked Chameleon.*
4: *Meller's Chameleon.*
5: *Giant Madagascar Chameleon.*
6: *Graceful Chameleon.*

Left: A graceful chameleon perched on a thin twig in Kenya's Tsavo National Park.

LIZARDS
Agile Reptiles

In addition to the major groups of lizards - the agamids, chameleons, iguanas and so on - there are a number of families either with fewer species or which are not so widespread as the others. They are nonetheless important with several of their representatives being particularly well known.

The skinks are one such group. Although enormously common throughout their range, with over 700 species, the skinks are not often seen. When skinks are observed, many people mistake them for snakes because of their appearance. Most species are found in semi-desert areas where they burrow in the loose, dry ground in search of invertebrates. Legs are something of an hindrance to this lifestyle, so the skinks tend to have small, almost insignificant legs. The less specialised species appear to be squat-bodied lizards with stumpy legs. When moving they often squirm their way across the ground rather than actually running.

The more extreme forms of skink have long, slender bodies and tiny, almost non-existent legs. These creatures spend most of their time underground where they move with a sinuous motion which has been likened to 'swimming through sand' by many observers. When surprised on the surface, the burrowing skinks vanish with surprising speed, seeming to sink directly into the ground with scarcely a movement. They find their insect prey by locating the vibrations which are created by the minute movements of termites or beetle larvae.

The five-lined skink of North America takes its name from the prominent markings which decorate the young. The stripes gradually vanish as the lizard approaches maturity, when it takes on a more uniform brownish tinge. The three-toed skink of the Iberian peninsula is also decorated with stripes, although in this species they persist into adulthood.

Glass snakes are another family of lizards which have reduced limbs. Indeed, their very name shows the close similarity between these lizards and snakes. The front limbs are entirely absent in glass snakes, but vestigial hind limbs protrude from the body. The closely related slow worm is entirely limbless. Growing to over 4 feet (1.2 metres) the glass snake preys upon rodents, lizards and other small creatures which it kills by biting. In cooler areas of its range, the glass snake hibernates with several individuals sharing a burrow.

The gila monster and the beaded lizard are the only two members of the family helodermatidae, and have acquired notoriety as the only poisonous lizards. Although potent, the poison is not particularly effective as the delivery system is poor. The poison glands are linked to grooves in the side teeth. When the gila monster bites poison flows into the mouth and is worked into the victim by chewing. The lack of an efficient injection system makes the poison of only marginal use.

Both species live in arid regions of America, emerging at night to prey upon rodents, eggs and fledglings. The gila monster ranges across New Mexico and Arizona while the beaded lizard is at home in Mexico. These creatures are voracious feeders, consuming vast amounts whenever the opportunity presents itself. When food is plentiful, the short, stumpy tail becomes greatly enlarged with stores of fat. When prey is scarce, the fat is consumed and the tail gradually returns to a more normal size.

The various species of wall lizard are found around the Mediterranean, though some are found as far north as the English Channel. As their name suggests, they are expert climbers, taking advantage of the slightest irregularity to find a toe-hold on walls and rocks. They spend long periods of time basking in the sun and are extremely active, fast-moving creatures. Preying on various invertebrates, especially earthworms, the wall lizards are not shy of humans and are often found near houses. During the winter the wall lizard hibernates in hollows and tunnels before emerging to breed in the spring.

The horned lizard is a small, specialized form which is heavily armoured against attack. The short, flat body is covered with tough, thick scales while the flanks and neck are protected by stout, sharp horns which are enough to deter any but the most determined predator. It uses its tongue to scoop up ants and other small insects. When frightened the lizard may squirt blood at an adversary from its eyes.

Above: A lava lizard from California. Left: Clark's spiny lizard which makes its home in Arizona's Sonoran Desert.

1: Beaded Lizard.
2: Collared Lizard.
3: Milos Wall Lizard.
4: Ocellated Skink.
5: Gila Monster.
6: Red Sand Lizard.
7: Three-toed Skink.
8: Five-lined Skink.
9: Lilford's Wall Lizard.
10: Iberian Wall Lizard.
11: European Glass Lizard.
12: Spiny-footed Striped Lizard.
13: Eyed Lizard.
14: Spiny-horned Lizard.
15: Schreiber's Lizard.
16: Grey Burrowing Lizard.

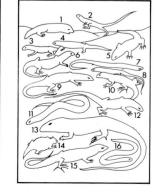

BOAS AND PYTHONS
The Suffocating Snakes

The largest snakes on earth are undoubtedly the giant constricting snakes, but exactly how big they can grow is a matter of some dispute. The largest snake to have been measured under scientific conditions was an Indian python nearly 33 feet (10 metres) long. However, the giant snakes of the Amazon are encountered under conditions where opportunities for scientific study are necessarily limited. Truly monstrous snakes are reported from isolated forest areas, but such tales, however well recorded, are treated as dubious by science. Perhaps the best documented such beast was one measuring 62 feet (19 metres), though less reliable reports speak of snakes twice that length.

Snakes first appeared on earth about 80 million years ago. These early snakes were non-poisonous and appear to have been very similar to the constricting snakes which today are commonly known as boas or pythons. Some scholars prefer to place the two types in a single family, the boidae, while others separate the pythons into a different family, the pythonidae. The anatomical differences between the two are slight compared with the similarities, being chiefly concerned with the arrangement of bones in the skull. More important is the fact that the pythons lay eggs while the boas retain the eggs inside the body until they hatch, thus giving birth to live young.

Most scientists regard the boas and pythons as the most primitive of the living snakes. They preserve features which clearly show the lizard ancestry of the snakes and which are lost in more advanced serpents. The skeleton shows a vestigial pelvic girdle and thigh bone in some species. The constricting snakes also have both lungs. In other groups the left lung is severely reduced or totally absent.

Constricting snakes also lack the venom glands and delivery systems of the more advanced snakes. Instead, they rely upon sheer brute strength to subdue their victims. When launching an attack, a constricting snake will either lie in ambush or stalk its victim. A favourite trick of some species is to wait in the branches of a tree for a suitable victim to pass by, and then drop directly on to it. Others lurk in bushes waiting for a target to come within reach.

With a sudden burst of speed, the snake dashes forward to grasp its quarry in its strong jaws. At the same time it attempts to throw a loop of its body around that of the prey. Often the very weight of the snake is enough to bring the victim to the ground, whereupon more coils are

slipped around the body. The snake then begins to squeeze. Contrary to popular belief, the constricting snakes do not crush their victims. Instead they suffocate them. Whenever the victim exhales, the snake tightens its grip making it impossible for the hapless quarry to breathe. When the prey has died, the snake will release its grip and manoeuvre itself so that it is in a position to swallow the prey whole. In common with other snakes, the boas and pythons are incapable of chewing and so have to swallow a victim in one go.

The feeding patterns which drive the snakes are little understood. After a heavy meal most snakes are sluggish and disinclined to hunt. It was presumed that increasing hunger eventually drove the snake to make another kill, which would then be followed by another lazy period. However, recent research disputes this. It has been found that some species alternate between long periods of starvation and what might best be described as a feeding frenzy. One individual went for over two years without a meal, but then consumed a large quantity in a short period of time.

The constricting snakes are found in most warmer areas of the world, but the two types have distinct distributions. The pythons are snakes of the Old World, being found across Asia, Africa and Australia. The boas, however, are most common in the New World, particularly the South American forests, but certain species are to be found in East Africa and parts of Asia.

The breeding habits of the egg-laying constricting snakes are fairly typical of most snakes. After mating, the pair separate. The female lays the eggs in a natural hollow in the ground where they are abandoned. The warmth of the surrounding air is relied upon to keep the embryos alive, while their safety from attack is simply a matter of chance. The behaviour of the Indian python, however, is very different. She selects a hollow similar to those favoured by other species and in it lays around 100 eggs. She then coils her body around the eggs. At intervals the snake ripples her muscles, thus shifting the eggs around. It is not clear whether the snake is merely guarding the eggs or if she is incubating them. Snakes are cold-blooded creatures which rely on their surroundings for warmth. However, readings taken from within the mound of eggs have shown that the eggs may be kept at a temperature some degrees higher than the surroundings. The young hatch out after two months, whereupon the mother loses interest and leaves them to fare for themselves.

1: Reticulated Python.
2: Indian Sand Boa.
3: Rainbow Boa.
4: Children's Python.
5: Green Tree Boa.
6: Amethyst Python.
7: Indian Python.
8: Madagascar Tree Boa.
9: Water Boa Anaconda.

Far left: The rainbow boa from Guyana in South America. Left: The African rock python photographed in Tsavo National Park in Kenya.

COLUBRID SNAKES
Three-Scaled Snakes

Perhaps the only certain thing which can be said about the colubrid snakes as a group is that they have three large scales between their eyes. It is this one feature which characterises all colubrids and sets them apart from other snakes. That apart the colubrids show a great diversity of size, habits and appearance which has led many to suggest that they are not a natural grouping at all, but merely a convenient taxonomic class into which may be fitted all snakes which do not obviously belong elsewhere. However, a widely accepted alternative has yet to be proposed so the artificial nomenclature of colubrid must be allowed to stand.

There are about 1,800 species grouped under the colubrid family, making this by far the largest of all the families. The colubrids are generally considered to be the first of the four advanced families of snake, the other three being the cobras, vipers and the pit vipers. Though the colubrids are an amazingly diverse group some generalisations can be made about their characteristics. The most telling are those which are common to all four families of advanced snakes, but the colubrids lack the sophisticated dentition and other features which distinguish the other families.

Snakes are descended from lizards, but the transformation from the legged reptile to the legless reptile has involved a number of specialisations and anatomical changes which are seen very clearly in the colubrids. It is thought that the lizard ancestors of the snakes originally lost their limbs as an adaptation to burrowing and only later was the body plan found to be of use above ground.

Such a hypothesis would explain much about the serpent anatomy, not least the enormously elongated body. This would clearly be easier to pull through loose soil than a shorter, squatter body which would have a larger cross-section and so involve a greater disturbance of earth. The complete lack of frills, casques and spines which are so common among lizards can also be seen as an adaptation to a burrowing lifestyle, for they would also have made progress through soil more difficult.

The eyes of snakes lack eyelids, instead they are covered by a transparent scale which seals them in. This would have enabled the snake to keep its eye open and yet protected underground. The unblinking and immobile eye of the snake gives it a peculiarly fixed stare which many humans find disconcerting. Indeed many snakes are credited with being able to hypnotise humans and other creatures so as to lure them within striking reach. It is sometimes rumoured that this alleged power is due to the foetid smell which is given off by some species. No hard evidence of any such power has ever been produced.

The adoption of an elongated worm-like body led to the rearrangement of internal organs and the skeleton. The standard reptilian body plan is one in which the body is basically short, deep and broad, very different from the serpentine body. The most obvious adaptation was one to greater length for the number of vertebrae was increased noticeably. There may be anything up to 400 individual bones in the vertebral column. In addition the bones are linked by special joints much stronger than those of more conventional reptiles.

The organs, too, needed to adapt to the new body plan. The most dramatic was the loss of the left lung. Having two lungs, separated by membranes and muscles is unnecessarily space consuming in a body as narrow as that of the snake. The left lung is absent from most colubrids, and severely reduced in the remainder, while the right lung has expanded in size so as to serve the full respiratory needs of the creature. The relative positions of the kidneys have likewise shifted so as to become better suited to a long, thin body.

Below: Grass snake, a European species which is also found in western Asia.

Having perfected a body suitable for burrowing, it is postulated, the snakes took to a life above ground as their peculiar talent for preying on small creatures came into its own. Once above ground, however, the snakes had to find a method of movement which did not involve legs. The most common solution was found in the mode of locomotion aptly known known as serpentine. In this the snake braces its body against any obstructions or irregularities in the ground. It pushes against these with strong muscular contractions so as to propel its body forward. When in a particularly confined space, the snake may twist its rear into a solid brace while pushing its head forward. The front of the body is then anchored and the rear pulled up. A third and much more dramatic movement is that known as sidewinding. Used chiefly by vipers, this involves throwing the body out in loops which touch the ground only at certain points. Muscular contractions shift the body sideways while fresh loops are thrown out. Sidewinding is most useful on soft surfaces, such as desert sands.

The lack of limbs presented another problem to the snakes, one of which required greater specialisations to solve. Lacking limbs with which to manoeuvre their prey it is impossible for snakes to bite chunks of flesh from a victim. Whatever creature could be caught had to be swallowed whole. Yet the snakes habitually take prey which is rather large in proportion to themselves. Snakes have developed a specialised jaw structure and digestive tract which enables just this type of swallowing to happen.

The lower jaw is connected to the skull by a series of lever and bony rods entirely unlike the jaw joint of any

1: Leopard Snake.
2: Common Garter Snake.
3: Grass Snake.
4: Four-lined Snake.
5: Horseshoe Snake.
6: European Whip Snake.
7: Corn Snake.
8: Milk Snake.

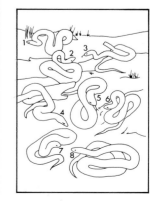

become highly active and bite the intruder. Less aggressive is the European whip snake which spends most of its time on the ground hunting for lizards, rodents and frogs. The corn snake, also known as the rat snake, is found in North America. Also inhabiting North America is the common garter snake which lives further north than any other New World snake, being found in British Columbia.

Some colubrids have a more sophisticated method of despatching their prey than the simple biting or constricting used by the others. These snakes have poison glands and are often grouped together in the subfamily boiginae. Known colloquially as back-fanged snakes, these snakes have a rudimentary poison delivery system. The poison glands are linked to large teeth set near the back of the upper jaw. The position of these teeth makes

other type of creature. This enables the snake to drop the jaw down so that the gape is quite extraordinarily large. The skin bordering the back of the mouth is especially elastic to cope with such drastic distortions. At the same time as the lower jaw drops, it also spreads for the two halves are connected by ligaments which allow a degree of outward movement.

Having achieved such a wide gape, snakes can obviously get their mouths around prey rather larger in circumference than themselves. However, lacking limbs with which to push the prey into the mouth this, in itself, would be of little use to the snake. The ability to swallow the victim rests on the ligaments connecting the two halves of the lower jaw. This allows the two halves to swing backwards and forwards independently of each other. While one half pulls the prey back a small amount, the other pushes forward for a fresh grip. This then pulls the victim back while the first swings forward in its turn.

Behind the jaw is an oesophagus and stomach which are able to expand hugely so as to envelope a prey much larger than they are themselves in their natural, relaxed shape. The digestive juices which are poured upon the swallowed victim once it is in the stomach are extremely powerful. They are capable of eating their way through the skin to reach the nutritious meat inside and even of breaking down the bones into useful minerals. Only hair is able to withstand the strength of these chemicals. Many snakes regurgitate a ball of fur when the digestion of a victim is complete. The semi-liquid paste of faeces which remains is passed out with the urine.

Most colubrid snakes have solid teeth which are fused to the jaw, but which are replaced periodically. They rely on their bite and their strength to subdue victims. The grass snake is a very common European species which can grow to over 6 feet (2 metres) in length. It is often found near water and is an extremely good swimmer. The bulk of its diet is made up of aquatic animals such as frogs, newts and fish, although it sometimes hunts on land taking rodents and small birds.

More fond of land animals is the ladder snake of southern Europe. This snake will spend long periods of time basking in the hot sun, but if disturbed will suddenly

it difficult to bring the venom to bear on the victim. The venom is rather more useful for subduing and finishing off a prey already seized than as an attack weapon in itself.

Typical of the back-fanged snakes is the mangrove snake which measures about 8 feet (2.5 metres) in length and is boldly marked in black and yellow. It moves through the branches of the mangrove trees which dominate the swampy estuaries of southern Asian rivers. Also counted among the back-fanged snakes are the various species of king snake which prey on other snakes, one of the few prey with a suitable shape for easy swallowing. Most of the venomous colubrid snakes are not dangerous to man for their teeth are not well placed for delivering venom and the poison itself is usually not very potent. An exception is the boomslang of Africa which has a particularly violent poison and fangs set further forward than is usual.

Top left: A coiled copperhead snake. Top right: The speckled king snake. Above: Leptophis snake from Mexico.

COBRAS
Hooded Killers

The cobra family, the elapids, contains some of the most dangerous and venomous snakes in existence. Indeed, of the 250 or so species each includes members capable of killing creatures many times larger than themselves, and most are deadly to humans.

The secret behind the extraordinary deadliness of the elapids is to be found in their venom glands and in their fangs. The poison of the elapids is a modified form of saliva which is produced in glands analogous to the saliva glands of constricting snakes. In some species the poison producing glands are extremely large, the Malaysian coral snake has glands reaching back beyond its skull to extend about a quarter the length of the body. When the snake bites, muscles surrounding the gland contract, pumping poison into the victim through hollow fangs placed well to the front of the jaw.

One interesting variation on this poison delivery system is found in the spitting cobras, including the ringhals cobra. These snakes have the poison exit holes on the front of their fangs rather than at the tips. When the muscles around the venom glands contract, the poison is forced down the tooth and forwards out of the mouth for a distance of up to 8 feet (2.5 metres). This seems to be a defence mechanism for if the snake is approached by a larger creature, and cannot slide away unnoticed, it will rear up to face the intruder. If the creature does not retreat at once, the cobra 'spits' its venom. The snake is capable of aiming accurately and projects its poison at the target's eyes. Instantly a sharp burning pain sears the eyes, causing a blindness which is usually temporary but may be permanent.

Cobras are probably best known for the skin flaps which can be expanded behind the head to form a sinister hood. This hood has no doubt enhanced the cobra's deadly reputation. The hood is made up of about twenty pairs of ribs which are flat, rather than curved and can be spread out to display the broad flap of skin with its distinctive markings which serve to identify the species.

The hood is seen best as the snake prepares to strike, though most would not consider remaining long enough to study it closely under such circumstances. When preparing to strike at a prey, the cobra lifts its head and hood up into a vertical position and then begins to sway from side to side. This is probably so that the snake can gauge more accurately the distance and location of the intended victim. Then suddenly, the head will shoot forwards and the teeth sink into the prey, delivering the poison.

Such elaborate manoeuvres do not characterise the cobra strike when it is disturbed. If trodden on or otherwise interfered with a cobra will strike at the first moving object it sees. It is this habit which causes the hundreds of human deaths attributed to cobras in Asia every year. The locals walk around barefoot and if they tread on a snake they have no protection against the bite. One explorer in South America before the First World War inadvertently gripped a cobra thinking it was a branch. The snake immediately struck at the person following, burying its fangs in his swinging tobacco pouch before making off.

The cobra which is responsible for more human deaths than any other is the Indian cobra, a 7 foot (2.2 metre) long snake which is found throughout southern Asia. It is no more venomous than other cobras, but is more dangerous because it frequents paddy fields and areas of growing grain where farmers are likely to come across them unexpectedly. Much larger is the aptly named king cobra of Malaysia, Indonesia and neighbouring areas. Growing to around 18 feet (5.5 metres) this is the largest poisonous snake in the world and is well able to kill and consume animals as big as pigs and small deer.

Below: A black spitting cobra with its head raised and hood extended in defensive posturing designed to frighten intruders away.

In addition to the true cobras, the elapid family also includes snakes more commonly referred to as mambas, kraits, and corals. The first of these are possibly the most dangerous to man. The various species of mamba live in the forests of central and southern Africa, moving through the trees in search of the small birds and reptiles on which they feed. Generally more slender than cobras, the mambas are extremely fast moving snakes able to race along thin branches to catch prey unawares. Their venom is extraordinarily toxic and is capable of killing a human within ten minutes, nor do they hesitate to attack, striking with great rapidity if they feel threatened.

The kraits are found in southeastern Asia and may claim several hundred human lives each year, though it is difficult to be precise with statistics from such remote areas. The coral snakes are more widely spread and are far more colourful than other elapids. Their bodies are typically banded with blacks, whites, reds and yellows in displays which can be extremely striking. It is not clear whether this is a type of dazzle camouflage, designed to disguise the shape of the snake, or whether it is a warning coloration to frighten off potential aggressors by advertising the venomous nature of the corals. They tend to be fairly secretive snakes which are active at night in search of rodents and other small prey.

1: Ringhals.
2: Forest Cobra.
3: Asian Cobra.
4: Albino Cobra.
5: Speckled Cobra.
6: Egyptian Cobra.
7: Black Mamba.
8: Coral Snake.
9: Green Mamba.
10: Spitting Cobra.

VIPERS AND PITVIPERS
The Striking Snakes

The vipers and pit vipers are usually placed in separate families, the viperid and crotalid respectively, but share many features and may be better considered as divergent groups of a single basic type. The most characteristic shared feature is to be found in the jaws and teeth and is chiefly concerned with getting the venom into the victim in the most efficient way possible.

The poison fangs of these snakes are much longer than in any other group, the gaboon viper having 2 inches (5 centimetre) long teeth. These teeth are located at the front of the jaw, as in cobras, but are hinged in order to lie flat along the line of the jaw when not in use. When the snake opens its mouth to strike, the bones at the front of the skull move forwards and twist up, so bringing the fangs into position. The extraordinary length of the fangs means that vipers and pit vipers do not need actually to bite their prey as do other snakes. They are able to inject a lethal amount of poison simply by striking and plunging the long teeth into the victim.

The poison which these snakes deliver is one of the most complicated and mixed known in nature. The clear liquid may contain several dozen different chemicals, though the actual make up varies from species to species. Whatever the form of the venom it seems to work in any one of four ways, or in a combination of methods. One constituent acts on the heart muscles of a victim, being carried there in the bloodstream. It causes the heart muscles to seize up, bringing about death by means of a heart-attack. A second type of venom acts directly on the blood, either inhibiting or causing it to clot. Either effect being potentially very dangerous. A third toxin included in the venom affects the nervous system causing either paralysis or a complete lack of co-ordination between mind and body. The final group of chemicals which may be found in cobra venom causes a general breakdown of body tissues with which it comes in contact. This last example is probably closest in action to the saliva from which the poisons are derived.

For delivering the venom to a victim the cobras have a system far more efficient than that of the venomous colubrids. The poison glands are connected via tubes to fleshy sheathes at the front of the upper jaw. These sheathes surround the bases of long, hollow fangs. The poison enters the fangs through a hole in the base inside the sheath and then runs down the tooth to emerge through a hole at the tip. When the snake bites, the exit hole is deep within the victim, so the poison enters as if it were being injected.

The viper group contains several of the better known species of poisonous snake, including the asp which many consider was the snake used by Cleopatra, Queen of Ancient Egypt, when committing suicide. Another common viper is the European adder which is found throughout Europe and deep into Asia. This is the only viper found in the British Isles and it is extremely aggressive, always ready to strike. Though cases of fatality are rare, the snake is one to be regarded with caution and bites should be treated as soon as possible.

The puff adders are short tailed vipers with comparatively thick bodies which may be six inches broad, although the length is barely 3 feet (1 metre). The heads of these snakes are also broader than is usual for they contain especially large venom glands from which quickly fatal doses are injected whenever the snakes strike. These dangerous serpents are restricted to Africa, though some non-poisonous New World species are commonly referred to as puff adders.

Far more deadly in the Americas are the pit vipers, a few species of which may be found in Asia. The group takes its name from a pair of sensory pits which are located just forward of the eyes. These are capable of detecting minute variations of heat, such as that given off by the warm bodies of rodents and other small mammals. By swaying their heads, the pit vipers are able to discern the location and size of a mammal by its heat alone, an ability particularly useful for the nocturnal hunts in which these creatures habitually indulge.

1: Indian Viper.
2: Rhinoceros Viper.
3: Asp.
4: Puff Adder.
5: Sand Viper.
6: Russel's Viper.
7: Horned Viper.
8: Gaboon Viper.
9: Rattlesnake.
10: Asian Pit Viper.
11: Pit Viper.
12: Adder.
13: Green Mottled Adder.

The best known of the pit vipers are the rattlesnakes, found in North America. Typically aggressive and highly venomous these snakes carry a rattle at the end of their tails which is made up of dead, horny segments. When the snake moves these rattle together quietly. The loud, ominous rattle is heard most often when the snake feels threatened. It shakes its tail to warn an intruding creature of its presence, and most intruders take the warning seriously enough to retreat before the snake strikes. When the snake is striking for food, of course, the rattle is not used.

One of the more unusual rattlesnakes is the sidewinder which is found in the desert states of the southwestern USA. Living in a habitat largely made up of sand, this snake has developed an unusual method of moving. It throws its head sideways, placing it down some distance from its body. By quickly rippling its muscles the snake is able to pull its body to the spot where the head was resting, while the head is thrown out again to begin a fresh move. In this way the snake travels rapidly across the sand leaving only a series of disconnected lines to mark its passing.

Left: A prairie rattlesnake rearing to strike. When the rattlesnake feels threatened it will sound its rattle before striking, but remains ominously silent when stalking prey.

NEWTS
The Fire Eaters

The amphibians were the first vertebrates to take to a life on land, leaving the water around 360 million years ago. Before that time the only vertebrates in existence were water-bound fish, while the dry land was the preserve of insects and other invertebrates. All later land vertebrates, including reptiles, birds and mammals were descended from the early amphibians.

Though the amphibians have been overtaken in evolutionary terms by the more advanced vertebrates, they have not been driven to complete extinction. Some 2,000 species of amphibian are in existence today, living in a range of habitats, though tending to prefer damper areas or dry places within easy reach of standing water. The giant forms of past ages have long since vanished, the largest modern species rarely reaching 4 feet (1.2 metres) and most being small enough to hold in one hand.

Though they are the products of hundreds of millions of years of evolution, the present day amphibians show many traces of their aquatic origins. The most obvious of these is in their method of reproduction. Apart from a few aberrant species which have developed specialised breeding mechanisms, all amphibians follow a common pattern.

After mating the female makes for water where she lays her eggs either singly or in large groups. From the egg hatches a larval form commonly termed a tadpole. Typically this is a small, round-bodied creature with a long tail, fringed for extra purchase while swimming, there are no limbs. The creature has external gills to extract oxygen from the water.

In the course of a few weeks the legs appear and the external gills vanish to be replaced initially with internal gills and later by lungs. The circulatory system changes drastically to cope with the new body plan. When these changes are complete the tadpole has metamorphosised into the adult form and leaves the water for the land. Many forms are herbivorous at hatching, but change to a high-protein carnivorous diet during metamorphosis. As adults, amphibians retain the moist skin of the juvenile which is, uniquely, permeable to both gases and liquids allowing the amphibians to breathe with their entire body surface.

The amphibians are divided into three orders, the caecilians, the newts and the frogs. Of these the rarest and least known are the caecilians, legless amphibians restricted to the tropical areas of the world. At first glance these creatures appear rather like worms for not only are they legless, but several species feature ring markings similar to segments. The similarity is taken further by their burrowing habits. Caecilians live by burrowing through the organic soils of tropical forests in search of insects, earthworms and other prey. They can be readily distinguished from earthworms, however, by their mouths and eyes. They find their victims chiefly by the use of small sensory nodules located beneath the eyes. A few species do not leave the water on becoming adult but lead a fully aquatic lifestyle. Other species are fully terrestrial, retaining the eggs within the mother's body until the young become miniature adults.

Better known and more widely spread are the newts, also known as salamanders. These amphibians have long, slender bodies with elongated tails, but move on legs, unlike the burrowing caecilians. In common with other amphibians, the newts tend to favour damp habitats where they feed upon invertebrates. Most reproduce in water, but the subsequent development of the individual tends to vary greatly. Most leave the water as adults to live on land, but a few species take to the land only to return to the water as aquatic adults later in life.

The range of the newts is very great. They are found throughout the Americas, Africa, Europe and Asia, inhabiting a range of habitats. One species is found high in European mountains, and uses the spring meltwater in which to breed. Other species are restricted to swamps and stagnant water.

The best known of all the newts is the fire salamander of European forests. According to old folktales the fire salamander could not only survive in the heart of fires, but positively enjoyed basking in flames. In the 18th century wars it was common practice to refer to particularly keen fire-eating soldiers as salamanders. In fact the fire salamander has no such preference and is as vulnerable to flames as is any other creature.

The bright markings on the skin of this and other salamanders is a protective measure. These creatures have glands in the skin which secrete a mucus which is slightly poisonous and highly irritating. Any predators which seize these creatures in their mouths suffer burning pains, which can also affect the eyes if the mucus touches them. The colourful patterns advertise the presence of the newts, allowing predators to recognise them and so avoid a potentially unpleasant encounter.

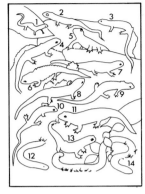

1: *Pygmy Salamander.*
2: *Care Salamander.*
3: *Redback Salamander.*
4: *Marbled Salamander.*
5: *Californian Newt.*
6: *Chinese Spiny Newt.*
7: *Tyrolean Taliangerisis.*
8: *Fire Salamander.*
9: *Red Salamander.*
10: *Spanish Salamander.*
11: *Tiger Salamander.*
12: *Slimy Caecilian.*
13: *Red-cheeked Salamander.*
14: *South American Caecilian.*

Left: A spotted salamander which is found in damp woodlands of the eastern United States and Canada but is a rather rare creature.

FROGS AND TOADS
Leaping Amphibians

Known collectively as the anurans, the frogs and toads make up the vast majority of amphibian species, some 2,500 of them. Though there is great variety between species, in appearance and habits, the anurans share a great many features which enables scientists to put them together in a single group.

The anurans are placed in the order Salientia which comprises five sub-orders and some 16 families. In common parlance these are divided into creatures which are either frogs or toads. Originally these terms were restricted to European frogs of the family ranidae and toads belonging to the family bufonidae and so had a valid taxonomic meaning. As vast numbers of new anurans have been discovered, belonging to a number of families and suborders, the names 'frog' and 'toad' have been applied more or less indiscriminately so that they now have little real meaning. Generally, however, frogs tend to be smaller and to have moister skins, though this is by no means a fixed rule.

Like other amphibians, the anurans show a strong liking for water and damp habitats. Their reproductive cycle is strongly tied to the water, though there are some notable exceptions. Unlike most amphibians, however, the anurans lack a tail. The adult form of all species conforms to a basic pattern. The body is short and squat and merges almost imperceptibly with the broad head. Internally the spine is short and stunted, with much of the rear part of the body being supported by a huge pelvis.

Attached to the large pelvis are a pair of long, muscular hind legs. When at rest these legs are kept folded along the sides of the body, but when moving the true length of the legs can be seen. Some species have becomes specialised leapers, the hind legs being used to launch the animal into the air. The front legs tend to be shorter and squatter. They are used either for crawling or to absorb the impact of landing from a leap.

Adult anurans are without exception carnivorous. Though some varieties show a preference for certain prey, such behaviour is not common. It is probably best to state that any creature small enough to be subdued is likely to be regarded as a likely victim by an anuran. The hands and tongue both play a role in hunting. Larger prey are seized in the hands and subdued by biting. Anurans do not possess poisonous bites, relying instead upon strength and tenacity to succeed. The bigger species of anurans are well able to attack and kill mammals as large as mice. The hands may also be used to cram earthworms and other creatures into the mouth.

Though they are likely to attack any creature of a suitable size, anurans have been seen to ignore certain creatures. These tend to be brightly coloured insects with venomous or noxious properties which the anurans find distasteful. Clearly the anurans are able to distinguish individuals and to avoid those they dislike.

Smaller victims, such as insects, may be caught by the tongue, which is coated in sticky secretions. Most species are capable of flicking out their tongues with great accuracy to entrap unsuspecting flies or moths. The tongue is rooted at the front of the mouth, and is usually carried folded back between the lower jaws. Glands in the tongue keep it permanently coated with gummy mucus, ready for use. The action of projecting the

tongue, entrapping the prey and withdrawing both to the mouth is accomplished is less than one tenth of a second.

Whatever the actual mechanism of catching the prey, the hunting technique varies little between species. Most of the time is spent simply sitting waiting at a suitable spot in the hope that a victim will chance by. When this happens the anuran positions itself so as to be able to launch an attack. The prey is stalked slowly, with the anuran advancing cautiously rarely moving more than one limb at a time in order to avoid alarming the target.

Though such a hunting technique tends toward the lethargic, anurans can be extremely active and even athletic when the need arises. If a passing victim appears to be moving just beyond the reach of a conventional stalk, it may be ignored or the anuran may spring into action, almost literally. Sometimes a quick dash across the intervening ground is enough to overtake the victim, but flying insects may be attacked in mid air. The more active frogs are well able to leap several inches into the air, flick out their tongues, and snap up flies or other passing insects.

Only when particularly hungry will most anurans consider actively seeking out food. Creeping slowly through their chosen habitat, the anuran moves in search of suitable prey. Some species have well-defined hunting territories and will patrol them regularly. When the site

1: *Phyllomedusa bicolour.*
2: *Phyllomedusa tomopterna.*
3: *Asian Flying Frog.*
4: *Hyla chrysoscelis.*
5: *Asian Tree Frog.*
6: *Barking Tree Frog.*
7: *Phyllomedusa trinitatis.*
8: *Australian Giant Tree Frog.*
9 - 15: *Poison Dart Frogs (various).*
16: *Australian Tree Frog.*
17: *Darwin's Pygmy Frog.*
18: *South American Tree Frog.*
19: *Coroboree Frog.*
20: *Marsupial Frog.*

Left: Dendrobates pumilia, a poison dart frog from Costa Rica. Below: Agalychnis callidryas from Panama.

of a previously successful hunt is reached, the anuran may settle down to await a victim. If none appears, the patrol is continued. When a potential prey is found, the standard hunting behaviour is brought into play.

A characteristic of the feeding anurans is a curiously exaggerated blinking when eating. When a meal is in the mouth, the anuran may close its eyes violently, lowering them into the skull at the same time. It has been conjectured that this is part of the mastication of the food. The dropping eyeballs being used to further squash such soft-bodied prey as worms. In fact, the blinking is a part of swallowing. As the eyeballs drop they push down into the mouth, forcing any object in the mouth down and back to the gullet.

The digestive system of the anurans is fairly simple, but perfectly adequate for their limited diet. While passing down the oesophagus to the stomach, the prey is coated with mucus. Once in the stomach, the food is attacked by enzymes which begin the breakdown of the victim. As the food passes through the intestine it is subjected to the action of alkalines and enzymes which concentrate on breaking down protein and emulsifying fats prior to absorption via the intestine walls to the blood. The blood carries nutrients first to the liver and then on to the rest of the body. The residue of the food, meanwhile, enters the cloaca where it mixes with urine before being expelled.

The breeding habits of the anurans are fairly consistent. In cooler climates, the breeding season opens in the spring when the warmer weather brings an abundance of food. The males call to the females from suitable ponds, producing the characteristic croaking and booming sounds of anurans. The calls serve not only to attract females, but also to space out the males so that they do not all congregate in one area.

When the female approaches she is grasped by the male in an embrace known as amplexus. The pair then swim together while the female lays her eggs, and the male fertilises them as they emerge. Some species deposit their eggs in one huge mass, others distribute them in a long string, wrapped around water-plants.

The eggs are soft and covered with protective jelly and are laid in vast numbers. The odds against the young surviving to adulthood are so high that hundreds of eggs need to be laid to ensure the survival of the species. After a few days the eggs hatch to produce small tadpoles which have external gills for respiration and long tails for swimming. The tadpoles feed on the water-plants, rapidly putting on weight until metamorphosis begins. The hind legs appear first, followed by the front legs together with such physiological changes as the loss of the gills and re-arrangement of the internal organs.

A few species of anuran do not follow this common pattern, but instead have developed more specialised breeding patterns which ensure a higher survival rate among the young. The midwife toad is one such species. When the male grips the female in amplexus, the eggs are not allowed to drop into the water. Instead the male gathers the newly fertilised eggs around his hind legs and rump, keeping them securely attached to his body. For the following three weeks or so, the male keeps to damp areas, immersing himself occasionally in water in order to keep the jelly-covered eggs moist. When the eggs have reached the point when the tadpoles are ready to emerge, the male discards the eggs in a suitable pond where the tadpoles are left to care for themselves. This action ensures that the eggs stand a better chance of reaching the hatching stage than do those of other species which are left in the water to the mercy of hungry fish.

Care for the eggs is taken to a higher point by the Surinam toad. The male of this species catches each of about 60 eggs as it is laid, fertilises it and then transfers it to the females back. Once all the eggs are positioned, the spongy skin of the female's back covers them, enclosing each in its own pocket. The developing young remain enclosed in their mother's back until they break out some 90 days later as tiny, but fully formed toads.

As small and plentiful creatures, the anurans form a rich food source for a large number of larger creatures. Birds, reptiles and mammals all prey upon anurans, with gourmet humans eating their share of frogs' legs. The frogs have developed two basic defences against predation. The first is to evolve camouflaged skins which help them to merge into their surroundings. Several species are able to change their coloration so as to match changing backgrounds, though this ability is not as well developed as in some reptiles, chameleons for example.

The second defence against predation is to take a quite different course and to become as conspicuous as possible. These frogs are generally rather small tropical varieties and are boldly marked in yellows, reds, greens, black and white. The safety of these species lies in the fact that their skin mucus contains chemicals which are either poisonous or caustic and which cause extreme discomfort to any predator foolish enough to attempt to eat one. Most hunters quickly learn to avoid brightly coloured frogs, which are thus left in comparative safety.

In tropical areas of the New World the local tribesmen have learnt how to take advantage of the gaudy frogs. They capture large numbers of these tiny amphibians and cook them so as to 'sweat' out the mucus. This is then collected and coated on to arrows making them extremely poisonous. The slightest scratch inflicted by such an arrow is potentially fatal. The frogs are thus responsible for possibly the earliest form of chemical warfare known to humans.

Oddities among the anurans are the flying frogs of the rain forests of Southeast Asia. These frogs are habitual tree dwellers which rarely leave their arboreal homes, except at breeding time. They cannot achieve true flight, but are expert gliders. They are able to drift effortlessly from tree to tree because of specialised features of their bodies. They are slender-bodied creatures with greatly enlarged feet which are fully webbed. When taking to the air, the frog spreads its outsize feet to act as parachutes, moving them slightly to control the direction and speed of the glide. It has been reported that these creatures can glide further horizontally than the distance dropped vertically.

1: Pleurodema sp.
2: Edible Frog.
3: Horned Toad.
4: Golden Toad.
5: Forest Toad.
6: Painted Escuerzo.
7: Brazilian Toad.
8: Couch's Spadefoot.
9: Midwife Toad.
10: African Bullfrog.
11: American Bullfrog.
12: Painted Frog.
13: Casque-headed Frog.
14: Mexican Burrowing Toad.
15: Fire-bellied Toad.
16: Red-spotted Toad.

Left: Argentinian horned frog which preys on other amphibians and some small mammals on the forest floor.

Index of Illustrators

Index of Photographers